MICROBIOLOGY & BIOTECHNOLOGY

Alan Cadogan

B.Sc., F.L.S., C. Biol., F. I. Biol.,
Teacher, Lecturer, Chief
Examiner at A Level and
Examiner of Projects at A/AS
Level, Series General Editor

John Hanks

B.Sc., C. Biol., M.I. Biol.,
Chair of Examiners for AS and
A Level Biology, Director of
Studies, Westcliff High School
for Girls, Essex

Nelson

D0186375

Thomas Nelson and Sons Ltd
Nelson House Mayfield Road
Walton-on-Thames Surrey
KT12 5PL UK

Nelson Blackie
Wester Cleddens Road
Bishopbriggs
Glasgow
G64 2NZ UK

Thomas Nelson Australia
102 Dodds Street
South Melbourne
Victoria 3205 Australia

Nelson Canada
1120 Birchmount Road
Scarborough Ontario
M1K 5G4 Canada

© Alan Cadogan and John Hanks 1995

First published by Thomas Nelson and Sons Ltd 1995
ı(T)ᴘ Thomas Nelson is an International Thomson Publishing Company.
ı(T)ᴘ is used under licence.

ISBN 0-17-448227-2
NPN 9 8 7 6 5 4 3 2 1

All rights reserved. No paragraph of this publication may be reproduced, copied or transmitted save with written permission or in accordance with the provisions of the Copyright, Design and Patents Act 1988, or under the terms of any licence permitting limited copying issued by the Copyright Licensing Agency, 90 Tottenham Court Road, London, W1P 9HE.

Any person who does any unauthorised act in relation to this publication may be liable to criminal prosecution and civil claims for damages.

Printed by Hobbs the Printers Ltd. of Southampton.

ACKNOWLEDGEMENTS

The authors and publishers would like to thank the University of London Examinations and Assessment Council for permission to reproduce the exam questions on pages 42, 72-3 and 86, The Associated Examining Board for the question on pages 42-3, *The Guardian* for the extracts on pages 21, 95 and 128, and *The Observer* for the extracts on pages 55 and 66. Thanks are also due to Smiles Brewery, Bristol, for their help, and the Open University for permission to redraw figure 23a from *Single Cell Protein* by Zbigniew Towalski (PS621 *Biotechnology*) on page 57, and figure 4.2 from *Science Matters: Genetic Engineering* by Norman Cohen and Hilary MacQueen (S280) on page 79.

Photographic material:
Dr Jeremy Burgess/Science Photo Library 2; David Scharf/Science Photo Library 4; Biophoto Associates 7; Menge and Wurtz/Biozentam, University of Basel/Science Photo Library 9 (left); A. B. Dowsett/Science Photo Library 9 (right); Institut Pasteur/CNRI/Science Photo Library 19; Omikron/Science Photo Library 20; Wellcome Institute Library, London 21, 65; Andrew Lambert 30, 49 (top right), 57, 59 (right), 60 (right), 68 (top); National Library of Medicine/Science Photo Library 40; J. Allan Cash Photo Library 44, 47 (c and d), 60 (left), 100; Inverawe Smokehouses, Taynuilt, Argyll 45 (left); H. P. Bulmer Ltd 45 (right); Alan Cadogan 47 (all except c and d), 50 (left); Cephas Picture Library 49 (left); Cephas/Mick Rock 49 (bottom right) and 52 (left); Middlebrook Mushrooms 50 (right); Cephas/Martin Walls 51; Sinclair Stammers/Science Photo Library 52 (bottom right); St Mary's Hospital Medical School/Science Photo Library 53 (left); Martin Cole 53 (right) and 54; David Hall/Science Photo Library 56; James Holmes/Celltech Ltd/Science Photo Library 58; National Dairy Council 59 (left); Science Photo Library 64; John Walsh/Science Photo Library 68 (below); Wessex Water 70; Phillippe Plailly/Euroelios/Science Photo Library 72, 83 (right); Peter Menzel/Science Photo Library 74; Horticulture Research International, East Malling 80 (left); Hank Morgan/Science Photo Library 80 (right); Rosi Waterhouse 81; American Association for the Advancement of Science (cover of *Science*, 18 November 1983) 83 (left); Linda Tyfield 85; Tony Brain/Science Photo Library 89; Dr Anthony Bryceson 91; Alfred Pasieka/Science Photo Library 92; Manfred Kage/Science Photo Library 96; Biozentam, University of Basel/Science Photo Library 112; John Beringer 129.

Cover photograph showing a commercial fermentation unit for the production of biological products such as interferons, using genetically engineered cultures of bacteria, viruses or microorganisms: Science Photo Library.

CONTENTS

General Editor's Introduction to the Series

Biology - Advanced Studies is a series of modular textbooks which are intended for students following advanced courses in biological subjects. The series offers the flexibility essential for working on modern syllabuses which often have core material and option topics. In particular, the books should be very useful for the new modular science courses which are emerging at A-Level.

In most of the titles in the series, one of the authors is a very experienced teacher (often also an examiner) and is sympathetic to the problems of learning at this level. The second author usually has research experience and is familiar with the subject at a higher level. In addition, several members of the writing team have been closely involved in the development of the latest syllabuses.

As with all textbooks, the reader may expect not to read from cover to cover but to study one topic at a time, or dip in for information as needed. Where questions are asked, an attempt should be made at an answer because this type of *active reading* is the best way to develop an understanding of what is read.

We have referred throughout to *Biological nomenclature - Recommendations on terms, units and symbols*, Institute of Biology, London, 1989. We are delighted to be able to thank the many friends and colleagues who have helped with original ideas, the reading of drafts and the supply of illustrations.

Alan Cadogan
General Editor

Authors' Introduction to Microbiology and Biotechnology

We wrote this book because of the fascination of the subject and its relevance to modern life. Microorganisms have played a central role in human life. On the debit side, they have been always with us as causes of disease in ourselves and in our domesticated animals and cultivated crops, as well as the spoilers of our produce and materials; on the credit side they have for millennia been important sources of food and sustenance.

We are now observing an even greater role of microorganisms in our lives. In the past two decades much of industry has been transformed by the harnessing of microorganisms for production, waste disposal, medical diagnosis, and even the refining of minerals. However, we are still in the very early stages of the biotechnological revolution. It would be a rash person who would attempt to predict its outcomes a decade hence.

In one week in mid-1995 the media reported on a new outbreak of the Ebola virus disease in Zaire, and the first deciphering of the entire genetic sequence of a freeliving organism (a bacterium with 1 830 121 DNA bases). There was also a criminal conviction, for stealing birds' eggs, based on DNA fingerprinting and the setting up of a national forensic DNA database in the UK.

The purpose of our book is to give you a first acquaintance with the intriguing world of microorganisms: their nature, the huge diversity of their structure and metabolism and above all their overwhelming importance to modern human life. We have included the requirements of all of the major examining bodies at this level and we hope that you will also find the account of biotechnology, and its background in microbiology, an enjoyable read for its own sake.

Alan Cadogan and John Hanks

INTRODUCTION – WHAT ARE MICROBES?

Mrs Robinson frowned in annoyance as she looked into the bread bin. 'Mouldy again: it must be the warm weather.' On the way to the pedal bin she felt a sneeze coming and reached for a Kleenex. 'Tchoo! Not too warm for a summer cold,' she grumbled to herself as she threw the bread and tissue into the bin. She was about to throw the potato peelings after them, but checked herself: they'd be for the compost heap, to help Bert's vegetables along.

Now, what else to get out before she called the family to tea? A diet yogurt for Sharon's dessert. At least her daughter had one small consolation for being diabetic, she had no trouble keeping slim.

In the bathroom, Sharon was dabbing her upper arm with a gauze pad soaked in alcohol, prior to her evening injection of insulin. She injected herself expertly, and as she put the little bottle of insulin back into the bathroom cabinet a phrase on the box caught her eye: 'Made from insulin crystals produced from recombinant DNA technology'. That sounded impressive; she wondered what it meant. She could hear Mum calling the family to tea: she used the toilet, flushed it and went downstairs.

Mrs Robinson could hear Bert coming in from the garden: she could also hear that he was in a bad mood. 'Those nasturtiums have wilted,' he announced bitterly as he pulled off his boots at the door. 'The watering they've had, and they've gone and ruddy well wilted.' He fetched a can of beer from the fridge, opened it and took a gulp. 'That's better,' he sighed. He paused reflectively. 'Must have been duff stock, those nasturtiums.'

Martin ran into the kitchen. 'Tea ready?' Without waiting for an answer he poured himself a large measure of orange squash. 'No wonder you're never quiet,' complained his father. 'I've read about this artificial colouring, tartra- whatever, makes kids hyperactive, they've proved it.'

Martin was reading the label on the squash bottle. 'No artificial colours, it says here,' he said. He scanned the list of ingredients. 'Colour: be-ta ca-ro-tene,' he read out.

'I expect that's just as bad,' muttered Mr Robinson. 'Anything on telly tonight?'

Sharon looked at the paper. 'There's a documentary at 8,' she said. 'Something about microbes.'

'Microbes?' said her father scornfully. 'The rubbish they put on. What on earth've microbes got to do with us?'

 Any answers to Mr Robinson's question? You should find ten.

Microbiology is the study of microorganisms (or microbes). These, however, do not form a single clear-cut group, but include any living thing that happens to be too small to see with the naked eye. A bacterium in a pot of yogurt, a mould growing on a slice of bread and a cold virus in someone's nose are all called microorganisms, but apart from their small size they have precious little in common with each other. (Note: some microbes which are too small to see reproduce in large numbers to form visible colonies such as mould spots on bread, or grow into a solid mass like a mushroom.)

To make sense of microorganisms we have to start by putting them into groups whose members do show genuine similarities beyond a coincidence of size. As a start, we can divide microorganisms into three very different groups:

• the **prokaryotic** microorganisms (bacteria and cyanobacteria)
• the **eukaryotic** microorganisms (protoctists and fungi)
• the **viruses**.

As we shall see, although the members of any one of these groups share a great deal in common with each other, differences between the groups are enormous.

DIVERSITY – PROKARYOTIC MICROORGANISMS

CHAPTER 1

Eukaryotes include all plants and animals, as well as the eukaryotic microorganisms described in Chapter 2. Prokaryotic cells differ from those of eukaryotes in many very clear-cut ways. Eukaryotic cells are larger, and contain a range of membrane-bound organelles absent from prokaryotes: these differences are summarised in Table 1.1.

Prokaryotes are classified into two major types: the **bacteria** and the **cyanobacteria** (or blue-green algae). Together they constitute the Kingdom Prokaryotae.

■ 1. BACTERIA

Bacteria were first observed and described by the Dutchman, Antony van Leeuwenhoek, in the late seventeenth century. Using a single lens mounted in a metal plate, van Leeuwenhoek examined materials such as the plaque from his own teeth, in which he was startled to discover enormous numbers of small, moving creatures that he called 'animalcules'. From his meticulous descriptions and drawings it is certain that at least some of the organisms van Leeuwenhoek saw were bacteria.

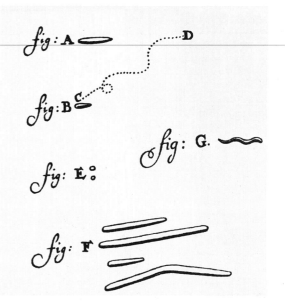

Antony van Leeuwenhoek's drawings of bacteria, 1683. We now know that A is a motile bacillus, B is *Selenomonas buccalis* and the track of its movement (C to D), E is micrococci, F is *Leptothrix buccalis* and G is a spirochaete, probably *Spirochaeta buccalis*, the largest one occurring in the mouth.

Feature	Prokaryotic cell	Eukaryotic cell
Typical diameter	0.2–5 μm	10–100 μm
Genetic material	Free in cytoplasm, as single loop of DNA plus plasmids; no membrane or envelope	Membrane-bound, in linear chromosomes wound around histones; no plasmids
Membrane-bound organelles	None	Mitochondria, chloroplasts, endoplasmic reticulum, Golgi apparatus
Cilia and flagella	No cilia; flagella when present a single filament	Cilia and/or flagella with '9+2' filaments may be present
Cytoskeleton	Absent	Present
Ribosomes	70 S	80 S

Table 1.1 Differences between prokaryotic and eukaryotic cells

2

The development of the light microscope during the eighteenth and nineteenth centuries allowed more and finer observations of bacterial cells. By the late nineteenth century, bacteria had been classified into groups according to their shape (Fig. 1.1a):

• the **cocci** (sing. coccus) were those with more or less spherical cells
• the **bacilli** (sing. bacillus) were those with stick-shaped or rod-shaped cells
• the **spirilli** (sing. spirillum) were those with twisted or spiral cells
• the **vibrios** were those with curved cells.

As well as their shape, the way in which individual cells were grouped together was also used as a means of classifying them (Fig. 1.1b):

• cocci that clung together like bunches of grapes were called **staphylococci**
• cocci that formed chains were called **streptococci**
• cocci that stuck together in pairs were called **diplococci**.

A further advance in describing and classifying bacteria came with the development in 1884 of **Gram staining**. The Danish bacteriologist, Christian Gram, first developed his staining procedure (see Fig. 1.2) as a way of making bacteria in infected animal tissues stand out from the surrounding animal cells. He found that when he stained infected animal tissue with a basic stain such as crystal violet,

and then washed the tissue with alcohol, the bacteria kept the stain but the animal cells did not. Only later was it discovered that some bacterial cells also lost the stain when washed with alcohol. This discovery neatly divided bacteria into those which are Gram-positive (retain crystal violet) and those which are Gram-negative (do not retain crystal violet).

Gram's accidental discovery proved of enormous value in classifying bacteria, but also showed that they could not be properly grouped by shape alone. Among the bacilli (rods), for example, there are Gram-positive types such as *Bacillus* and *Lactobacillus*, and Gram-negative types such as *Escherichia* and *Salmonella*. (In fact, it makes as little sense to place *Bacillus*, *Escherichia* and *Salmonella* in the same group because they are 'rod-shaped' as it would to place an eel, a snake and an earthworm in the same group because they are 'worm-shaped'.)

At first, classifying bacteria by their Gram staining reaction was a purely empirical procedure: that is, it was known that it worked, but there was no clear idea of the principle that lay behind it. Only much later (some 75 years after Gram's discovery) was it found that Gram-positive bacteria have a fundamentally different cell wall structure from Gram-negative ones. By then, however, the development of the electron microscope had revealed far more about bacterial structure than the light microscope ever could.

Cocci   Bacilli   Spirilli   Vibrios

Figure 1.1(a) Shapes of bacterial cells

Staphylococci   Streptococci   Diplococci

Figure 1.1(b) Groupings of bacterial cells

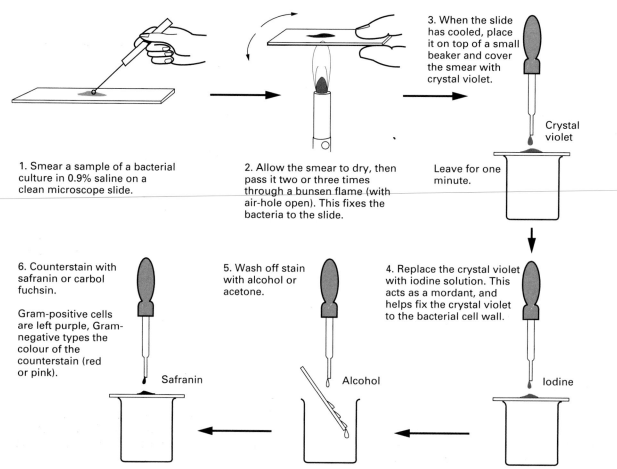

1. Smear a sample of a bacterial culture in 0.9% saline on a clean microscope slide.

2. Allow the smear to dry, then pass it two or three times through a bunsen flame (with air-hole open). This fixes the bacteria to the slide.

3. When the slide has cooled, place it on top of a small beaker and cover the smear with crystal violet.

Crystal violet

Leave for one minute.

4. Replace the crystal violet with iodine solution. This acts as a mordant, and helps fix the crystal violet to the bacterial cell wall.

Iodine

5. Wash off stain with alcohol or acetone.

Alcohol

6. Counterstain with safranin or carbol fuchsin.

Gram-positive cells are left purple, Gram-negative types the colour of the counterstain (red or pink).

Safranin

Figure 1.2 Gram staining technique

■ The fine structure of bacteria

The limitations of the light microscope lie not in its magnifying ability, but in its *resolving power*: that is, its ability to show very small structures very close together as separate objects, rather than as a single 'blob'. The resolving power of light microscopes is limited by the wavelength of light itself: even the finest light microscope simply cannot form an image of an object smaller than about 0.2 μm (200 nm) in diameter. Bacterial cells are typically about 1 μm in diameter, so light microscopes give perfectly good magnified images of whole bacteria, but are virtually useless for examining their internal structure.

```
Putting it in perspective: microbiological
measurements

1 m     = 1000 mm    = 1 000 000 μm  = 1 000 000 000 nm
(metre)  (millimetres)  (micrometres)    (nanometres)
so: 1000 nm = 1 μm = 0.001 mm (diameter of a bacterium)
```

The electron microscope forms images using a tightly focused beam of electrons instead of light. An electron beam has a very much shorter wavelength than visible light, so its resolving power is correspondingly greater, and an electron microscope can resolve objects of about 1 nm diameter. This has made it possible to examine the internal structure of bacteria in detail.

The electron micrograph shows a thin section of *Bacillus cereus*, a common Gram-positive rod.

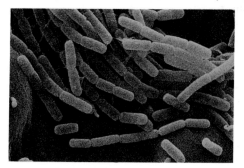

Electron micrograph of *Bacillus cereus*

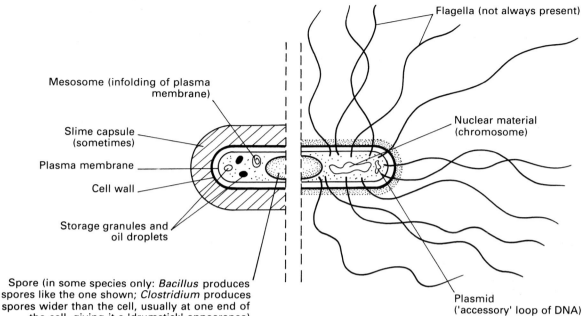

Flagella (not always present)

Mesosome (infolding of plasma membrane)

Slime capsule (sometimes)

Plasma membrane

Cell wall

Storage granules and oil droplets

Nuclear material (chromosome)

Spore (in some species only: *Bacillus* produces spores like the one shown; *Clostridium* produces spores wider than the cell, usually at one end of the cell, giving it a 'drumstick' appearance)

Plasmid ('accessory' loop of DNA)

Figure 1.3 Bacterial structure

The diagram of bacterial structure in Fig. 1.3 is a 'composite', based on many such micrographs and showing the features of bacteria in general rather than one type in particular. Half of the cell in Fig. 1.3 is shown with a capsule, the other half with flagella: bacteria may have one or the other of these, but not usually both (and some have neither).

■ The bacterial cell wall and slime capsule

The cell wall makes up 25–35% of a bacterial cell's dry mass. It is chemically complex, and nothing like the cellulose wall of plant cells. Its importance to the life of the cell is borne out by the fact that the antibiotic penicillin exerts its lethal effect on growing bacteria by interfering with wall synthesis. The wall's function seems, however, to be entirely mechanical, keeping the cell the same size and shape whatever the osmotic concentrations around it.

The main chemical component of the wall is **peptidoglycan** (otherwise called **mucopolysaccharide**). This is a compound formed from two sugar derivatives, N-acetylglucosamine and muramic acid, combined with tetrapeptides (chains of four amino acids). Uniquely, the tetrapeptides often include D-isomers of amino acids. These are only ever found in bacterial cell walls and

capsules: all other naturally occurring proteins and peptides consist of L-amino acids. Figure 1.4 shows how these components are built up into cross-linked peptidoglycan chains, giving the cell wall its complex architecture and its great structural stability.

As mentioned earlier, the walls of Gram-positive bacteria have a different structure from those of the Gram-negatives. In Gram-positive types (Fig. 1.5a), the peptidoglycan wall is 70–100 nm thick; in the Gram-negatives (Fig. 1.5b), there is only a thin layer of peptidoglycan (less than 5 nm), and outside it a unique 'outer membrane' consisting of a phospholipid bilayer containing **lipopolysaccharide** (a lipid-carbohydrate complex). This not only makes the two kinds of bacteria react differently to the Gram stain, but gives other important differences as well. In many Gram-negative species the lipopolysaccharide acts as an **endotoxin** (see page 91), giving rise to inflammation and other reactions in the human body. Many antibiotics penetrate Gram-positive walls much more easily than Gram-negative ones, making infections with Gram-negative bacteria more difficult to treat. In addition, Gram-negative bacteria are less susceptible to the action of **lysozyme**, an anti-bacterial enzyme secreted into tears, saliva and sweat.

5

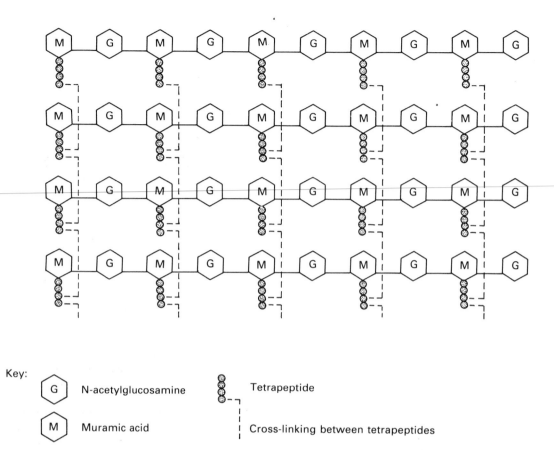

Key:

G — N-acetylglucosamine

M — Muramic acid

Tetrapeptide

Cross-linking between tetrapeptides

Figure 1.4 Structure of peptidoglycan layer of bacterial cell wall

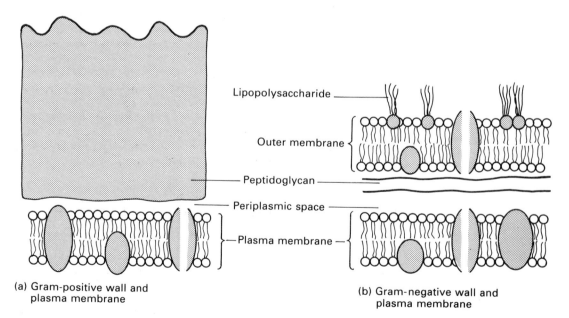

Lipopolysaccharide

Outer membrane

Peptidoglycan

Periplasmic space

Plasma membrane

(a) Gram-positive wall and plasma membrane

(b) Gram-negative wall and plasma membrane

Figure 1.5 Cell walls of Gram-positive and Gram-negative bacteria

Protection against lysozyme is probably one of the functions of the slime capsule found outside the cell wall of many disease-causing bacteria. It probably also protects them against ingestion by white blood corpuscles (phagocytosis). In many disease-causing species, mutants which lose the ability to produce a capsule also lose their ability to infect. This is true, for example, of *Diplococcus pneumoniae* which causes a form of pneumonia.

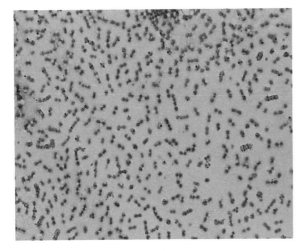

Capsules of *Diplococcus pneumoniae*

The capsule is made of polysaccharide, polypeptide or of a mixture of the two, depending on the food source being used. Some bacteria produce capsules only when growing on specific substrates, suggesting that in these examples at least the capsule is not so much an essential component of the cell as an excretory product.

■ Membranes

The **plasma membrane** of a bacterial cell has the same basic structure as that of a eukaryotic cell, and many of the same functions: in particular, it has the function of controlling the entry and exit of materials to and from the cell. However, the bacterial plasma membrane also contains the enzymes and carriers of the respiratory electron transport chain, and in that respect resembles more the inner membrane of the mitochondrion, an organelle present in eukaryotic cells but absent from bacteria. (This, together with the self-replicating nature of mitochondria, gives considerable weight to the hypothesis that mitochondria themselves are the distant descendants of once-independent bacteria living symbiotically within the cytoplasm of the early ancestors of eukaryotic cells.)

Many electron micrographs of sections of bacterial cells show the plasma membrane at the cell's equator folded into a complex structure called the **mesosome**.

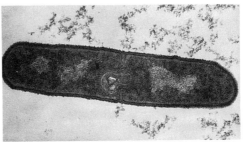

Section of bacterial cell showing mesosome

The mesosome has been implicated in numerous functions within the cell, including the separation of daughter chromosomes at cell division, cell wall synthesis, and respiratory activity. In this last connection, the mesosome could be seen as analogous to the cristae of mitochondria, increasing the area of membrane available for the electron transport chain, and thereby increasing the capacity of the cell for aerobic respiration and oxidative phosphorylation. There is, however, disagreement among microbiologists concerning the nature, the functions and even the existence of the mesosome: some believe that photographs showing mesosome merely show artefacts, created during preparation of the cell for electron microscopy.

Photosynthetic bacteria contain a further system of interal membranes, the **chromatophores** or **photosynthetic lamellae** that carry a photosynthetic pigment. In the purple photosynthetic bacteria lamellae are formed by infoldings of the plasma membrane, sometimes forming stacks that resemble the grana of eukaryotic chloroplasts. In green photosynthetic bacteria, the membranes form spherical vesicles with no apparent connection to the plasma membrane. The role of the lamellae and their pigments in bacterial photosynthesis is explained in Chapter 4 (page 25).

■ Cytoplasmic inclusions

Bacterial cytoplasm as revealed by electron microscopy appears to have a less organised structure than that of eukaryotic cells, lacking in particular the *compartmentalisation* given by membrane-bound organelles such as mitochondria and endoplasmic reticulum. The small size of prokaryotic cells presumably means that the enzyme-catalysed reactions of their metabolism can proceed quickly enough through random collisions within the general cytoplasm, without the need to concentrate particular enzyme and substrate molecules in any more confined space. However, some structures can be seen in bacterial cytoplasm. **Storage granules** vary from species to species, but commonly consist of a polymerised fatty acid called polyhydroxybutyrate, or of starch-like or glycogen-like polysaccharides.

As a rule, any one species stores energy in polyhydroxybutyrate (as in *Bacillus*) or as polysaccharide (as in *Escherichia*), but not in both forms. In addition, many bacteria accumulate inules, and **sulphur** droplets are found in the cytoplasm of the so-called purple sulphur bacteria, which live on energy released from the oxidation of hydrogen sulphide (see page 25).

As well as storage granules, bacterial cytoplasm always contains a large number of free **ribosomes**, which, as in eukaryotic cells, are the sites of protein synthesis. Bacterial ribosomes are smaller than those of eukaryotes. In an ultracentrifuge they sediment at 70 Svedberg units (70 S) rather than the 80 S characteristic of the bigger eukaryotic ribosomes. In actively growing cells, the ribosomes are seen to be organised into spiral clusters (polyribosomes), connected by fine threads of (presumably) mRNA.

■ Flagella and locomotion

Bacterial flagella (plural of flagellum) are quite different from those of eukaryotic cells such as mammalian sperms. They measure only 12–20 nm across compared with 500 nm for a eukaryotic flagellum. Most of the flagellum consists of a long filament made of protein called flagellin. This is attached by a short, rigid 'hook' to the 'motor' of the flagellum embedded in the cell wall and plasma membrane. Figure 1.6 shows the organisation of a flagellum from a Gram-positive bacterium: the 'motor' of Gram-negative bacteria is similar but a little more complex.

Unlike those of eukaryotic cells, bacterial flagella are driven entirely from the base. The 'motor' can rotate the flagellum either clockwise or anticlockwise. Experiments have shown that anticlockwise rotation has the effect of twisting the bacterium's flagella into a thick bundle that acts as an efficient propellor, driving the bacterium along in a more or less straight line. Clockwise rotation, on the other hand, unravels the bundle and the separate motions of all the flagella make the cell tumble in all

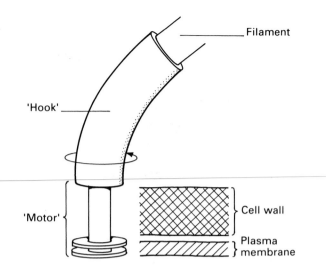

Figure 1.6 Base of flagellum of a Gram-positive bacterium such as *Bacillus*

directions (Fig. 1.7). Which way the flagella spin at any one time is controlled by receptor-molecules in the plasma membrane that respond to molecules such as food. Detection of a food concentration gradient triggers anticlockwise rotation, driving the bacterium up the gradient towards the food.

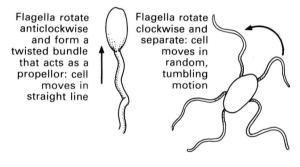

Flagella rotate anticlockwise and form a twisted bundle that acts as a propellor: cell moves in straight line

Flagella rotate clockwise and separate: cell moves in random, tumbling motion

Figure 1.7 Action of bacterial flagella

Ⓠ What would be the most advantageous response of the bacterial flagella if the cell were surrounded on all sides by a high concentration of food molecules?

■ Nuclear material and plasmids

The largest single inclusion in the bacterial cytoplasm is the single chromosome or **nucleoid**, visible in electron micrographs as a fuzzy, somewhat fibrous region.

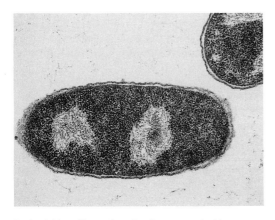

Escherichia coli bacterium showing two nucleoids

In many micrographs, two or more separate nucleoids may be seen: this probably results from DNA replication proceeding faster than cell division in rapidly growing cultures. The nucleoid is a single, tightly wound loop of DNA, containing all the genes essential for the cell's growth, survival and reproduction. Information is encoded in bacterial genes exactly as in eukaryotic DNA, using the same base triplets to represent the same amino acids. However, the bacterial chromosome contains none of the introns (non-coding regions) that break up the genes of eukaryotes, and unlike the latter, bacterial genes are grouped on the chromosome into orderly clusters called **operons**. The genes in a single operon are all concerned with a common function (for example, the metabolism of a single sugar or amino acid), and are all 'switched on' or 'switched off' by a single 'trigger'. Nothing resembling operons has been found in eukaryotic chromosomes.

For many years it was thought that the bacterial chromosome consisted only of naked DNA, contrasting again with the complex nucleoprotein structure of eukaryotic chromosomes. However, it has been shown that treatment of bacterial chromosomes with protein-digesting enzymes causes them to spread out, losing their tightly wound structure. This suggests that proteins play some role in coiling bacterial chromosomes into a size and shape compact enough to fit inside the bacterial cell. 'Unwound', the chromosome of *Escherichia coli* measures about 1 mm, 500 times the length of the cell containing it.

As well as this single 'main' chromosome, a bacterial cell may contain varying numbers of small additional loops of DNA called **plasmids**. These do not as a rule carry genes which are essential for the bacterium's life, but rather genes associated with survival under extreme conditions. For example, genes giving resistance to antibiotics are generally found on plasmids, a fact given greater medical significance by their ability to replicate and to be transferred from one bacterial cell to another, even between bacteria of different species. Plasmids can also temporarily join with the main chromosome, and when they 'unjoin' may take chromosomal genes with them: these in turn may be replicated with the plasmid and passed on to other bacterial cells. Plasmids are of enormous importance as carriers (vectors) of transferred genes in genetic engineering, a topic covered more fully in Chapter 9 of this book (page 77).

It is clear from this brief introduction that bacteria enjoy considerable genetic flexibility, picking up and passing on 'accessory' genes and even chromosomal genes in a manner which seems to break all the rules taken for granted among eukaryotes. The very concept of a species, which can satisfactorily be defined only by its genetic isolation from other types, is wholly undermined by the observed ease with which plasmids can be transferred between bacterial 'species'.

■ 2. CYANOBACTERIA

Because they carry out photosynthesis in a way similar to algae and higher plants, cyanobacteria used to be called 'blue-green algae' and classified with the rest of the algae. Their prokaryotic cellular organisation, however, clearly allies them with the bacteria. Like the green and purple photosynthetic bacteria, the cells of cyanobacteria contain membranes bearing photosynthetic pigments.

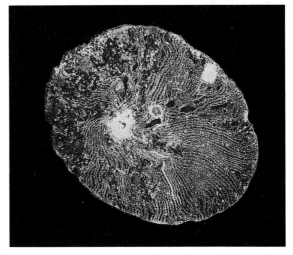

Cyanobacterium, *Spirulina platensis*, showing membranes

In the case of cyanobacteria, the membranes form stacks similar to the thylakoid membranes of chloroplasts: so similar, in fact, that it is widely believed that the chloroplasts of higher plants are themselves descended from once-independent cyanobacteria that took to living symbiotically inside other cells (just as some do today). (See *Biology Advanced Studies – Biochemistry*.)

Q Research the other evidence supporting the 'endosymbiotic' theory for the origin of chloroplasts. What other cell organelles are believed to have originated in a similar way? (See the scientist file on page 81.)

Modern cyanobacteria are variable in form and structure. Their cells are commonly spherical or cylindrical, sometimes helical, often forming long slimy filaments (Fig. 1.8). Most of the cells in these filaments are identical and completely independent, but filaments of some species may contain enlarged thick-walled cells called heterocysts, in which nitrogen fixation occurs (see page 28). Some filaments also develop thick-walled resting spores (**akinetes**), resistant to drought and high temperatures.

Reproduction in cyanobacteria is solely asexual, by cell division and in filamentous forms by fragmentation (physical breaking up of filaments).

Although most of the 1500 or so known species are aquatic, cyanobacteria can also be found on damp soil or rocks, and even attached to the fur of slow-moving animals (e.g. the sloth of South America, which appears to have green fur). The ability of many species to fix nitrogen from the atmosphere makes them ecologically important as producers in nitrate-deficient aquatic habitats. Other extreme habitats colonised by cyanobacteria include Arctic ice and hot springs. One type, *Spirulina*, inhabits salty alkaline lakes in Mexico, where since Aztec times it has been harvested and baked into cakes for human consumption.

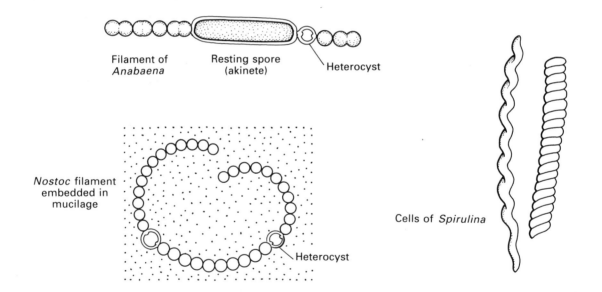

Filament of *Anabaena*

Resting spore (akinete)

Heterocyst

Nostoc filament embedded in mucilage

Heterocyst

Cells of *Spirulina*

Figure 1.8 Cyanobacteria

2 DIVERSITY – EUKARYOTIC MICROORGANISMS

Eukaryotic microorganisms fall into two distinct groups, each so large and so different from other life forms that they are treated as separate Kingdoms, on the same level as animals and plants. The **Protoctista** are the unicellular eukaryotes, including the organisms that used to be grouped as 'Phylum Protozoa' within the animal kingdom and many of those formerly classified as 'Algae' within the plant kingdom; whilst the **Fungi** include moulds, yeasts and familiar organisms such as mushrooms, toadstools and brackets.

■ THE PROTOCTISTA

Broadly, the 'animal-like' protoctists are grouped together as the **Protozoa**, while the 'plant-like' protoctists form the **Chlorophyta**. A third group, the **Euglenophyta**, has members with some animal-like and some plant-like characteristics. (The brown and red seaweeds - **Phaeophyta** and **Rhodophyta** - are also protoctists, although not microbes.)

ORGANISM FILE: *Amoeba proteus*

Description: rhizopod protozoan; no fixed shape, produces numerous temporary cell extensions (pseudopodia) for locomotion and for engulfing food; cytoplasm divided into clear, jelly-like ectoplasm (gel) surrounding granular, fluid endoplasm (sol).

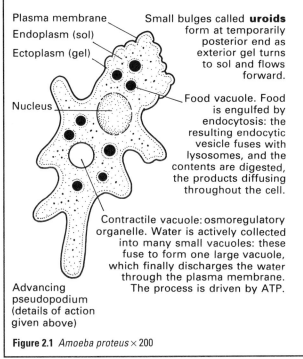

Plasma membrane
Endoplasm (sol)
Ectoplasm (gel)

Small bulges called **uroids** form at temporarily posterior end as exterior gel turns to sol and flows forward.

Nucleus

Food vacuole. Food is engulfed by endocytosis: the resulting endocytic vesicle fuses with lysosomes, and the contents are digested, the products diffusing throughout the cell.

Contractile vacuole: osmoregulatory organelle. Water is actively collected into many small vacuoles: these fuse to form one large vacuole, which finally discharges the water through the plasma membrane. The process is driven by ATP.

Advancing pseudopodium (details of action given above)

Figure 2.1 *Amoeba proteus* × 200

The conversion of gel into sol and vice versa underlies the organism's characteristic method of locomotion. It is thought that in the sol state **actin microfilaments** (part of the cytoskeleton of eukaryotic cells) are jumbled and disorganised, but in the gel they are arranged in regular arrays. Conversion between sol and gel is brought about by assembling or dismantling these arrays:

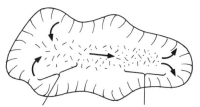

Microfilament arrays breaking down, gel changing to sol

Actin microfilaments forming into regular arrays, sol changing to gel

Figure 2.2 Diagram of cytoplasmic streaming

Mammalian white blood cells move in the same way, as do many other cells (for example the sperm of some molluscs).
Habitat: freshwater ponds and ditches.
Importance: a formative influence in the early education of generations of biologists!
Relatives: Many amoebae live in fresh and salt water, in soil and in animal guts. One of the latter, *Entamoeba histolytica*, causes amoeboid dysentery in humans.

■ Protozoa

The main groups of Protozoa are identified by their means of locomotion:
• the **Rhizopoda** move by cytoplasmic streaming, 'flowing' into cellular extensions called pseudopodia (see Fig. 2.3a and the organism file on *Amoeba proteus* on page 11)
• the **Zoomastigina** (flagellates) move by means of one or a few long flagella (Fig. 2.3b)
• the **Ciliophora** (ciliates) move by means of the coordinated beating of many short cilia (Fig. 2.3c)
A fourth group, the **Apicomplexa**, is more varied in form, and consists entirely of parasites. One of its most important members is the malarial parasite *Plasmodium*, described in detail in the organism file on page 99.

■ Chlorophyta

These single-celled 'green algae' are the main producers of aquatic ecosystems, both freshwater and marine. They show many of the features of higher plant cells, including cellulose cell walls and chloroplasts which contain chlorophylls *a* and *b*. A typical example is *Chlorella vulgaris*, discussed in the organism file on page 13.

(a) Rhizopoda (see also the organism file on page 11)

(i) *Entamoeba histolytica*, causes of amoebic dysentery, seen with ingested red blood cells (× 1400)

(ii) A foraminiferan, × 20. These amoebae secrete many-chambered shells, with pores through which pseudopodia protrude for food capture. Chalk is largely made from the skeletons of ancient foraminiferans

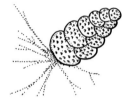

(b) Zoomastigina. The flagellate protozoa include some important parasites of humans and other animals. The flagella, of which one or several may be present, are of the '9+2' pattern typical of eukaryotes.

(i) *Trypanosoma gambiense*, × 1700. This flagellate causes trypanosomiasis in humans and other mammals: in humans the disease is also called sleeping sickness. The parasite is transmitted from host to host by a biting insect, the tsetse fly

(ii) *Trichomonas vaginalis*, × 1800. This is the cause of trichomoniasis, a sexually transmitted disease of humans (see Chapter 10, page 91)

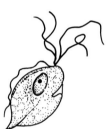

(c) Ciliophora. This group includes the largest and most complex single-celled organisms alive, probably representing the highest possible level of internal organisation that can be achieved with only one cell. They commonly have specialised areas for the entry of food and expulsion of undigested remains (cytostome and cytoproct respectively), and often two nuclei: a large **meganucleus** whose genes are involved in running the cell, and a small **micronucleus** used for sexual reproduction. The group includes both fixed colonial forms such as *Vorticella* (i) and free-swimming animals such as *Paramecium* (ii). Both are common in ponds and ditches.

(i) *Vorticella* × 75

(ii) *Paramecium* × 200

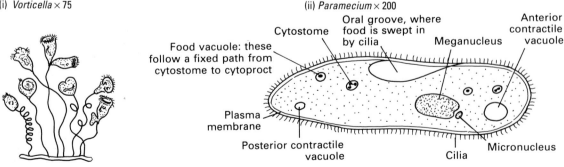

Figure 2.3 Some representative Protozoa

ORGANISM FILE: *Chlorella vulgaris*

Description: green alga (Chlorophyta) consisting of single more or less spherical cells, 5-10 μm in diameter. Cell wall thin, chloroplast cup-shaped, usually with a distinct **pyrenoid** (centre of starch production).

Only asexual reproduction occurs, with division of protoplast into 2, 4, 8 or 16 spores, which are liberated by the rupture of the parental cell wall.

Habitat: ponds, ditches, damp soil.

Importance: Chlorella and its relatives form the base of the food chain in many freshwater habitats. It is an important experimental organism (e.g. in the discovery of the Calvin cycle).

Relatives: Pleurococcus and *Protococcus* form the green powdery covering found on damp walls and tree-trunks. Other Chlorophyta include filamentous forms with cylindrical cells, such as *Spirogyra*, and motile, flagellate forms such as *Chlamydomonas*. Most of these can reproduce sexually as well as asexually.

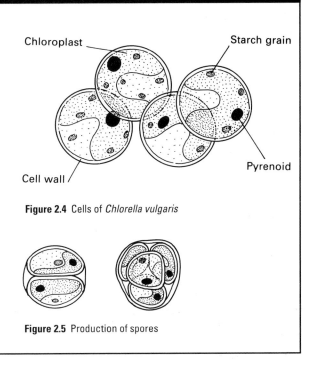

Figure 2.4 Cells of *Chlorella vulgaris*

Figure 2.5 Production of spores

■ Euglenophyta

The euglenoid protoctists differ from the Protozoa in the possession (usually) of chloroplasts, and differ from the Chlorophyta in the absence of a plant-like cell wall: instead, the outer covering is a thick **pellicle**, rigid enough to give shape to the cell but also flexible. Most are capable of photosynthesis, but none is fully autotrophic, as they require B vitamins from their environment. Some species are entirely heterotrophic. Locomotion is by the lashing of a single long flagellum: a second short flagellum is present, but has no direct role in locomotion, having been modified as a light-seeking organelle. The structure of a typical euglenoid is shown in Fig. 2.6.

Oomycota (water moulds and mildews) were previously classified as fungi (see Oomyctes, page 15). One of the best known, *Phytophthora infestans*, causes late blight of potatoes and led to famine in Ireland in the nineteenth century and mass emigration.

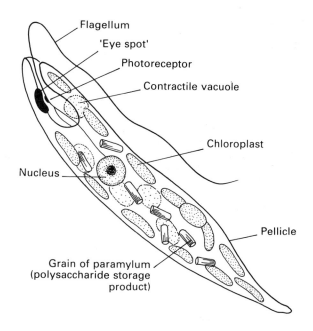

Figure 2.6 *Euglena gracillis* × 900, a typical member of the Euglenophyta. As the organism swims it rotates around its long axis: if there is light from one side, the shadow of the pigmented 'eye spot' falls on the photoreceptor once every rotation, causing the organism to jack-knife towards the light.

■ FUNGI

For many years, fungi were classified as a group within the plant kingdom. However, because they differ hugely from plants (and all other organisms) in their structure, chemistry and physiology, they are now, rightly, given a kingdom of their own.

A typical fungus is made up not of cells but of tiny branching threads called **hyphae**. The tangled mass of hyphae that make up one individual fungus is called its **mycelium**. Like cells, hyphae contain cytoplasm bounded by a plasma membrane; like plant cells, they also contain vacuoles, and are surrounded by a wall. However, only in some lower fungi does the wall contain cellulose: in most species, the main component of the wall is **chitin**, a tough material also found in insect exoskeletons. The presence in hyphae of membrane-bound nuclei and of organelles such as mitrochondria clearly identifies fungi as eukaryotic organisms. They never, however, contain chloroplasts. All fungi are heterotrophic: most are saprophytic, obtaining organic materials from dead and decaying remains,

whilst many are parasites of animals or of plants. In either case, their hyphae grow into and throughout the food source, secreting digestive enzymes from the tips and absorbing the soluble products of digestion. Saprophytic fungi are of enormous ecological importance in the recycling of dead plant material, as many of them produce enzymes such as cellulases (which catalyse the breakdown of cellulose) and lignases (which catalyse the breakdown of wood). These enzymes are rare among bacteria, which are thus less important in decomposing plant remains.

Fungi are classified according to:
(i) whether or not their hyphae are divided up by cross-walls (**septa**)
(ii) how they produce their sexual and/or asexual **spores**.

The Lower Fungi are those whose hyphae have no cross-walls (i.e. they are **aseptate**); the Higher Fungi have **septate** hyphae, with cross-walls (septa) perforated by holes (pores) - see Fig. 2.7.

Aseptate hypha

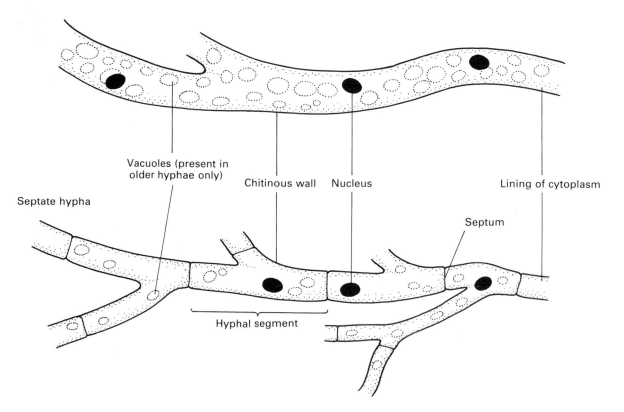

Vacuoles (present in older hyphae only)

Chitinous wall   Nucleus

Lining of cytoplasm

Septate hypha

Septum

Hyphal segment

Figure 2.7 Fungal hyphae × 1000

14

Within these broad divisions, the main groups are as follows.

Lower fungi

Oomycetes (now generally accepted as protoctists and called Oomycota, see page 13): aseptate hyphae; asexual spores motile by means of flagella; sexual reproduction forms a resting spore from the fertilised egg. Includes some important plant parasites, such as *Phytophthora infestans*, cause of potato blight.

Zygomycetes (Zygomycota): usually aseptate hyphae; asexual spores non-motile, usually produced in a sac called a **sporangium**; sexually produced spores made by fusion of two specialised hyphal branches called **gametangia**. Includes many familiar moulds - see the organism file on *Mucor mucedo*, page 16.

Higher fungi

Ascomycetes (Ascomycota): septate hyphae, septa pierced by simple pores (holes); asexual spores (**conidia**) bud off from tips of specialised hyphae; sexually produced spores made in groups of eight, in a cylindrical sac called an **ascus** (Fig. 2.8).

Yeasts, though not made of hyphae, are classed as Ascomycota - see the organism file on brewer's yeast (*Saccharomyces cerevisiae*), page 17.

Basidiomycetes (Basidiomycota): septate hyphae, septa pierced by complex **dolipores** (page 18); asexual spores (conidia) when formed; sexually produced spores made in groups of four on specialised structures called **basidia** (Fig.2.9).

Basidiomycetes often form large-scale structures for spore dispersal, including mushrooms, brackets and puff-balls. See the organism file on the field mushroom (*Agaricus campestris*), page 18.

Deuteromycota (Fungi Imperfecti): a rag-bag group for species in which sexual reproduction is unknown. Septate hyphae; asexual spores (conidia), like ascomycetes. Important members include *Penicillium* (Chapter 6, page 52), *Aspergillus* (Chapter 7, page 60) and *Fusarium* (see the organism file on page 123).

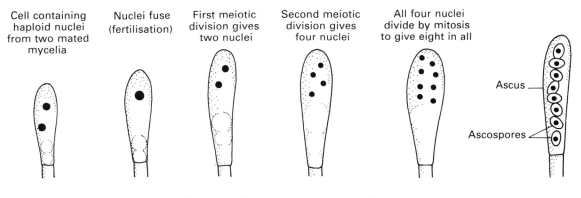

Figure 2.8 The development of ascospores. Each nucleus forms an ascospore, arranged in a row within a cylindrical ascus. The ascospores are released when the ascus breaks open, and each can form a new mycellium on germination. In some types, like *Sordaria* and *Neurospora*, the order of the ascospores in the ascus reliably preserves the sequence of divisions (meiosis I, meiosis II or mitosis): this has been important in genetic studies.

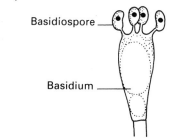

Figure 2.9 The development of basidiospores

ORGANISM FILE: *Mucor mucedo*

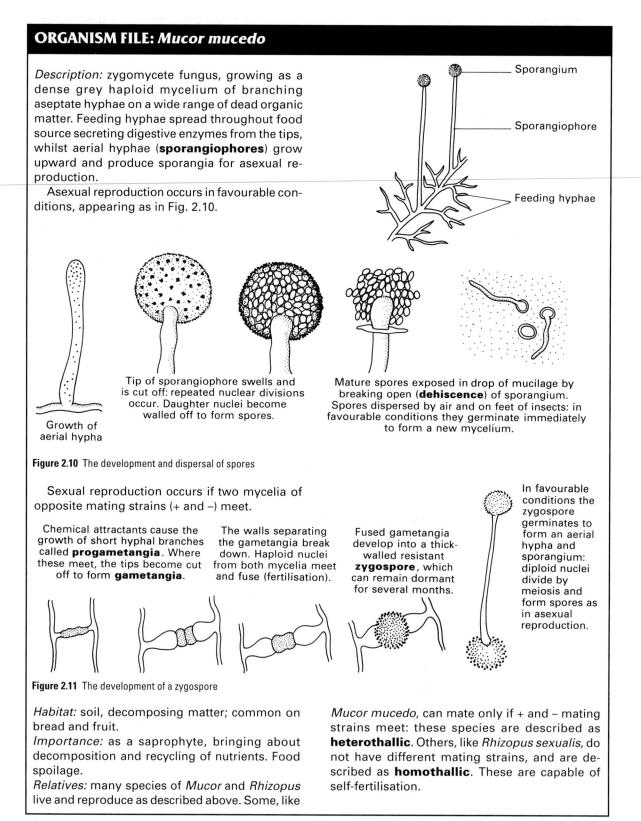

Description: zygomycete fungus, growing as a dense grey haploid mycelium of branching aseptate hyphae on a wide range of dead organic matter. Feeding hyphae spread throughout food source secreting digestive enzymes from the tips, whilst aerial hyphae (**sporangiophores**) grow upward and produce sporangia for asexual reproduction.

Asexual reproduction occurs in favourable conditions, appearing as in Fig. 2.10.

Sporangium

Sporangiophore

Feeding hyphae

Growth of aerial hypha

Tip of sporangiophore swells and is cut off: repeated nuclear divisions occur. Daughter nuclei become walled off to form spores.

Mature spores exposed in drop of mucilage by breaking open (**dehiscence**) of sporangium. Spores dispersed by air and on feet of insects: in favourable conditions they germinate immediately to form a new mycelium.

Figure 2.10 The development and dispersal of spores

Sexual reproduction occurs if two mycelia of opposite mating strains (+ and –) meet.

Chemical attractants cause the growth of short hyphal branches called **progametangia**. Where these meet, the tips become cut off to form **gametangia**.

The walls separating the gametangia break down. Haploid nuclei from both mycelia meet and fuse (fertilisation).

Fused gametangia develop into a thick-walled resistant **zygospore**, which can remain dormant for several months.

In favourable conditions the zygospore germinates to form an aerial hypha and sporangium: diploid nuclei divide by meiosis and form spores as in asexual reproduction.

Figure 2.11 The development of a zygospore

Habitat: soil, decomposing matter; common on bread and fruit.

Importance: as a saprophyte, bringing about decomposition and recycling of nutrients. Food spoilage.

Relatives: many species of *Mucor* and *Rhizopus* live and reproduce as described above. Some, like

Mucor mucedo, can mate only if + and – mating strains meet: these species are described as **heterothallic**. Others, like *Rhizopus sexualis*, do not have different mating strains, and are described as **homothallic**. These are capable of self-fertilisation.

Description: ascomycete fungus, consisting of separate cells rather than a mycelium.

For most of the life cycle, cells are diploid, reproducing asexually by budding. A bud is formed when the cytoplasm and plasma membrane bulge out through a weak point in the cell wall: mitosis occurs, and a daughter nucleus enters the bud.

The full life cycle has both a haploid and a diploid phase. Yeasts are heterothallic (i.e. they exist as different haploid mating strains). Commercial strains of brewer's and baker's yeasts have been produced by crossing strains which differ in their size, growth rate and tolerance of ethanol.

Habitat: commercial strains entirely domesticated; wild relatives occur on fruit and in soil.

Importance: as facultative anaerobes, yeasts like this ferment sugar to ethanol and carbon dioxide: this is of fundamental importance in baking, brewing and wine-making (see Chapter 6).

Relatives: yeasts are abundant in soil and water, and on plants and animals: they form the familiar misty 'bloom' on fruit such as plums, and some form part of the normal microbial flora of human skin and mucous membranes (see the organism file on *Candida albicans*, page 93). Not all are closely related to *Saccharomyces*, and some are not even ascomycetes: for example, the so-called mirror yeasts are degenerate basidiomycetes.

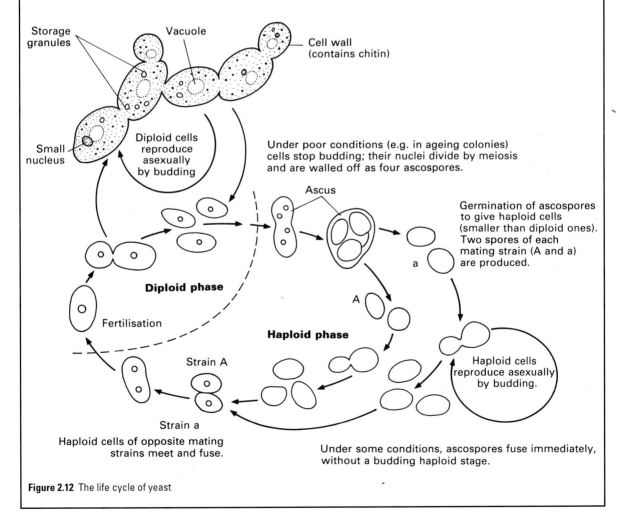

Figure 2.12 The life cycle of yeast

ORGANISM FILE: *Agaricus campestris*, the field mushroom

Description: basidiomycete fungus growing as a haploid **primary mycelium** in soil. Mating between mycelia of compatible mating strains gives rise to a **secondary mycelium**, each hyphal segment containing nuclei from both parents: this is also called a **dikaryotic mycelium**. Dikaryotic mycelia produce fruiting bodies (the familiar 'mushrooms') on which basidiospores are produced.

Habitat: open fields with abundant organic material in soil.

Importance: widely consumed and appreciated as part of human diet, though nutritional content is minimal. (See the case study on page 50.)

Relatives: cultivated mushroom, *Agaricus bisporus* (produces only two basidiospores on each basidium); horse mushroom, *Agaricus arvensis*; many other mushroom and toadstool-forming species, some edible, most inedible, some highly toxic to humans (such as Death Cap, *Amanita phalloides*): you should never eat any mushroom without being *certain* what kind it is!

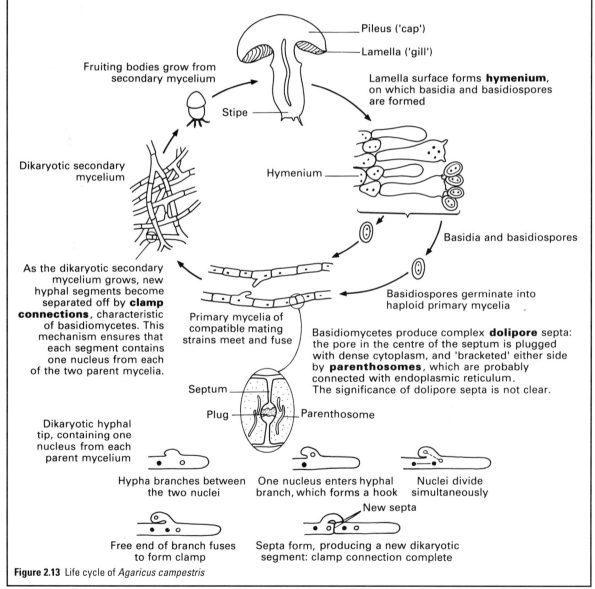

Pileus ('cap')

Lamella ('gill')

Fruiting bodies grow from secondary mycelium

Lamella surface forms **hymenium**, on which basidia and basidiospores are formed

Stipe

Dikaryotic secondary mycelium

Hymenium

Basidia and basidiospores

As the dikaryotic secondary mycelium grows, new hyphal segments become separated off by **clamp connections**, characteristic of basidiomycetes. This mechanism ensures that each segment contains one nucleus from each of the two parent mycelia.

Primary mycelia of compatible mating strains meet and fuse

Basidiospores germinate into haploid primary mycelia

Basidiomycetes produce complex **dolipore** septa: the pore in the centre of the septum is plugged with dense cytoplasm, and 'bracketed' either side by **parenthosomes**, which are probably connected with endoplasmic reticulum. The significance of dolipore septa is not clear.

Septum

Plug

Parenthosome

Dikaryotic hyphal tip, containing one nucleus from each parent mycelium

Hypha branches between the two nuclei

One nucleus enters hyphal branch, which forms a hook

Nuclei divide simultaneously

New septa

Free end of branch fuses to form clamp

Septa form, producing a new dikaryotic segment: clamp connection complete

Figure 2.13 Life cycle of *Agaricus campestris*

3 VIRUSES

Viruses are neither prokaryotes nor eukaryotes: they are not even made of cells, consisting instead of a small amount of nucleic acid (DNA *or* RNA, never both) enclosed in a simple protein coat with sometimes an outer envelope of lipid. The protein coat is called the **capsid**, and is made up of a fixed number of protein molecules called **capsomeres**. The capsid often has a simple geometrical symmetry - commonly an icosahedron or a helix - but some viruses, such as some of the **bacteriophages** that infect certain bacterial cells, have much more complex structures (Fig. 3.1).

The capsid and the nucleic acid together make up the **nucleocapsid**. The complete particle, including the lipid envelope where present, is called a **virion**, and is the form in which viruses exist outside living cells.

The size of all known virions is below the limit of resolution of the light microscope, so they can be seen only in images formed using the electron microscope. Small virions such as those of poliovirus have a diameter of about 25 nm, those of large viruses such as vaccinia a diameter of 200–300 nm.

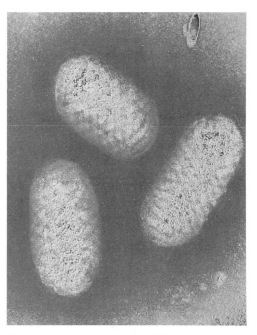

Transmission electron micrograph (TEM) of vaccinia virus particles

Icosahedral capsid of herpes virus × 400 000

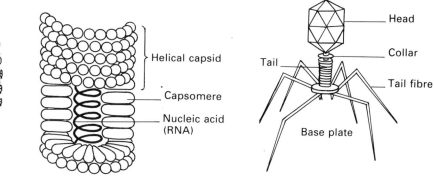

Helical capsid

Capsomere

Nucleic acid (RNA)

Part of helical capsid of tobacco mosaic virus × 1.24 million

Head

Collar

Tail

Tail fibre

Base plate

Bacteriophage T4 × 128 000

Figure 3.1 Virus structures

A virion by itself shows none of the usual characteristics of living organisms: it cannot move, it cannot reproduce, and it has no metabolism. It is activated only when it enters a living cell, usually a particular kind of cell in a particular plant or animal species. In the host cell, the virus sheds its protein coat, and its nucleic acid 'hijacks' the cell's metabolism, shutting down its normal functions and diverting it to replication of viral nucleic acid, synthesis of viral proteins and the assembly of new virions. These are eventually released, either by exocytosis or by the complete break-up (lysis) of the host cell.

Q Viruses are said to *replicate*, rather than to reproduce. What is the difference?

The replication of a DNA virus, *Herpes simplex*, is described in the organism file on page 22. The DNA of *Herpes simplex* is double-stranded, like that of cellular organisms and most other DNA viruses, but some viruses (the parvoviruses and certain bacteriophages) are unusual in having single-stranded DNA. In all cases, the DNA is replicated using host cell enzymes and raw materials.

Most of the viruses that have RNA as their nucleic acid have it in single-stranded form, as it is usually found in cells, but a few (the **retroviruses**) have double-stranded RNA. In cells (whether prokaryotic or eukaryotic), RNA is never replicated but always synthesised from a DNA template: host cells therefore contain no enzymes for the direct replication of RNA. Because of this, viral RNA has to contain genes coding for enzymes (RNA-dependent RNA polymerases or *replicases*) that enable it to be replicated. In the *negative-strand* RNA viruses (such as the influenza virus), the infecting RNA strand does not itself contain any useful genetic information, only the complementary strand produced on replication codes for any proteins, so that in these viruses the replicase enzymes must be packaged in the virion.

All viruses that infect plants have RNA as their nucleic acid (see page 124). Those infecting animals include DNA viruses (such as *Herpes simplex*), RNA viruses (such as those causing mumps, influenza and rabies) and retroviruses (such as Human Immunodeficiency Virus, HIV, and the cancer-causing Rous sarcoma virus). Retroviruses are RNA viruses that do not replicate their RNA directly, but instead transcribe it 'backwards' into DNA. This is the precise opposite of what occurs in cells (where transcription *always* involves producing RNA which is complementary to a DNA template), so

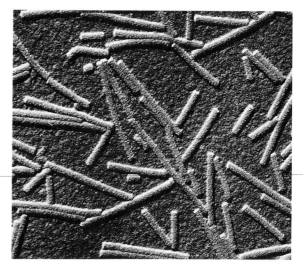

Micrograph of the rod-shaped Tobacco Mosaic Virus (TMV)

once again retroviruses have to provide their own enzymes to catalyse the process. In this case, the enzyme is *reverse transcriptase* (RNA-dependent DNA polymerase), which is packaged in the nucleocapsid along with the RNA, rather than being synthesised from scratch when the virion infects a cell. In the host cell, reverse transcriptase brings about the synthesis firstly of a single strand of DNA complementary to the viral RNA, and then of the DNA's complementary strand, thus completing the double helix. The viral DNA is then incorporated into a host chromosome, where it can remain latent for an indefinite time, in the manner described for *Herpes simplex* (page 22), or where it can be transcribed back into viral RNA for the synthesis of new virions. The replication cycle of a retrovirus (HIV) is shown in Fig. 11.6, page 111.

Q What important technological application has been found for the viral enzyme reverse transcriptase? (If in doubt, see Chapter 9).

Bacteriophages (viruses that replicate within bacteria) include both DNA and RNA viruses. The best known are the so-called 'T-even' bacteriophages, T2, T4 and T6. All three infect *Escherichia coli*, and have been intensively studied. Bacteriophage T4 is the subject of the orgamism file on page 23.

Q In this book, several viruses have been allocated 'organism files'. What are the arguments for and against viruses being regarded as organisms?

Doctor Edward Jenner (1749-1823)

Jenner was born the eighth child of the vicar of Berkeley, Gloucestershire. As a child he was inoculated against smallpox and suffered a moderate attack. He remained in the area for the rest of his life as a successful and popular country doctor. He was an experimenter and made discoveries in medicine and natural history but is best known for following up the rumour that milkmaids who suffered from a condition known as cowpox (caught from lesions on the udders of cows they were milking) seemed immune to the more virulent disease smallpox. At that time probably a third of all childhood deaths were from smallpox. The people who recovered from smallpox were disfigured by 'pock marks'. Jenner was anxious to find a cure. First he inoculated a group of milkmaids who had previously had cowpox with smallpox and must have been most relieved when they showed no symptoms. He then carried out an experiment in which he inoculated a young boy with the material taken from a cowpox sore on the hand of one Sarah Nelmes. Two months later he inoculated the boy with smallpox which, he wrote, 'as I ventured to predict produced no effect'. This was in 1796. He was honoured abroad yet remained in his village freely vaccinating the poor countryfolk. His work was publicised and led to mass vaccinations. The last natural case of smallpox was in Somalia in 1977 and in 1980 The World Health Assembly declared that the disease had been eradicated globally. An interesting ethical point is that in 1994 scientists met to decide whether the last two remaining laboratory cultures of the virus should be destroyed – the first planned extinction of a species!

VIROLOGY

Pox for the chop

Smallpox – there hasn't been a case anywhere in the world for 16 years – may at last be about to become truly extinct. The decision was taken by World Health Organisation experts late last week and the dirty deed will be done in 1995. Although one of the world's most wretched and disfiguring plagues was eliminated by dedicated teams of international experts in the late seventies, two little samples of the virus have existed in the US Centres for Disease Control in Atlanta, Georgia, and the Russian State Research Centre for Virology in Koltsovo.

And for years now, virologists the world over have been debating the future of these two little vials of death-in-the-offing. There has already been one stay of execution. The last date was December 31. The next tentative date for execution is June 30, 1995. The irony is that mankind could be casually, and arbitrarily wiping out species at the rate of up to 100 a day, just by destroying habitats. Smallpox, however, will be the first fellow-species on the planet to be put to death deliberately.

The medical experts have hung onto smallpox for more than a decade on a just-in-case basis: it was possible to imagine circumstances in which they would need samples of the live virus. But geneticists have been producing harmless clones of DNA fragments of the virus and are satisfied that they now have the full genetic blueprint that will enable them to conduct diagnostic tests with complete accuracy even after the virus itself is eliminated.

Death Row, for smallpox, is a padlocked freezer in Atlanta in a tiny room under constant electronic surveillance. The other condemned vials sit near Moscow, in liquid nitrogen at minus 94°F, guarded by policemen. The mere existence of the little beast has remained a constant worry: it wiped out half the Aztec nation in the 16th century; it ravaged George Washington's troops at Valley Forge. It killed Pharoah Rameses V in 1157 BC. In 1950, in India alone, it was killing a million people a year, and more than a billion people were permanently at risk. It killed one in five, and blinded or disfigured those who survived. It was eliminated by a campaign conducted by the WHO. There has already been one laboratory disaster: after an escape in Birmingham, one person died, and another committed suicide.

But the final step still worries some scientists. "We are just beginning to understand the functions of the genes of viruses that belong to this class," said one virologist. "It may be that five years from now, or 10 years from now, we will have a question and we will either need access to the DNA of the smallpox virus, or the smallpox virus itself."

The Guardian, 15 September 1994

ORGANISM FILE: *Herpes simplex* virus

Description: DNA virus. DNA double-stranded, 150 000 base pairs, relative molecular mass 5–7 $\times 10^7$. Protein coat (capsid) 110 nm in diameter, composed of 162 identical protein units (capsomeres) arranged in a regular icosahedron. Capsid surrounded by a lipid envelope, derived from host cell, giving total diameter 180–200 nm. Removal of the lipid envelope (for example by dissolving it with ether) makes the virus particles non-infective. It appears to be necessary to allow the virus to enter host cells.

Habitat: replicates in human cells, especially at boundaries between skin and mucous membranes (e.g. lips, female genitals); latent infection often persists after first symptoms have disappeared.

Importance: most commonly seen in *cold sores*, small watery sores (*papules*) around the lips. The fluid they exude contains many virus particles, and is highly infectious. Infection with *Herpes simplex* usually occurs in early childhood, but only about 10% of people infected show symptoms: the rest of the time the virus is *latent*, its DNA integrated into the host cell nuclei (Fig. 3.4). After this latency has become established, the virus can become activated at any time by injury or during periods of stress, causing cold sores to appear again. (As the name suggests, exposing the face to cold air can trigger them.)

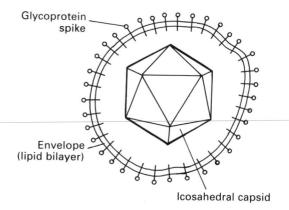

Figure 3.2 The *Herpes simplex* virus

Although cold sores are trivial, *Herpes simplex* virus can cause a much more serious infection in new-born babies, with widespread cell death and tissue damage, especially in the liver. This is often fatal, and survivors are likely to be permanently handicapped.

Relatives: A similar virus, *Herpes varicella-zoster*, causes chickenpox in children. In some cases the virus migrates through nerves serving the infected area of skin, and remains latent in neurones. Later injury or stress may reactivate the latent virus, which travels back down the nerves to cause the painful skin condition called shingles.

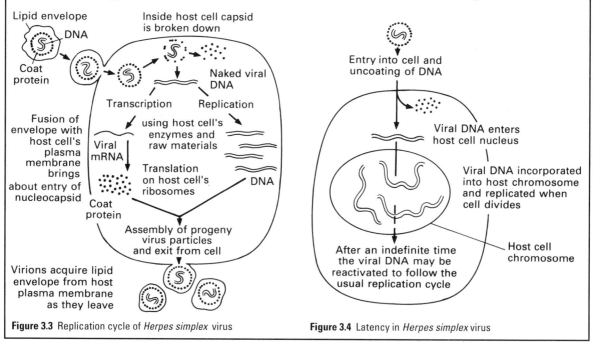

Figure 3.3 Replication cycle of *Herpes simplex* virus

Figure 3.4 Latency in *Herpes simplex* virus

ORGANISM FILE: Bacteriophage T4

Description: DNA virus with complex capsid consisting of distinct 'head' and 'tail'. Head hexagonal in cross-section, about 1000 protein molecules enclosing double-stranded DNA. Tail has a hollow core, 8 nm diameter, surrounded by contractile sheath of 16 nm diameter. Base plate of tail contains lysozyme for dissolving bacterial cell walls. Pins on base plate attached to tail fibres, 130 nm long, bearing recognition sites for surface antigens of bacterial hosts.

Habitat: replicates within cells of bacteria such as *Escherichia coli*. After initial attachment of tail fibres, lysozyme in tail plate dissolves a hole in the host cell wall: the tail sheath contracts, injecting the phage DNA from the head into the bacterial cytoplasm:

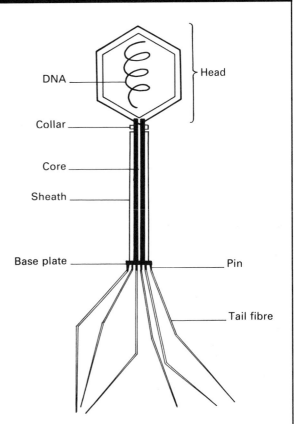

Figure 3.5 Phage T4 × 260 000

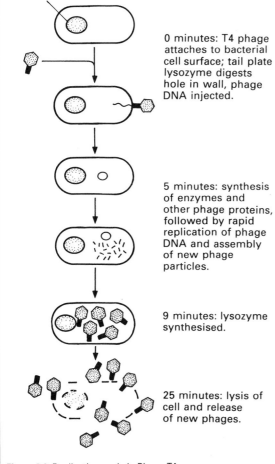

Bacterial chromosome

0 minutes: T4 phage attaches to bacterial cell surface; tail plate lysozyme digests hole in wall, phage DNA injected.

5 minutes: synthesis of enzymes and other phage proteins, followed by rapid replication of phage DNA and assembly of new phage particles.

9 minutes: lysozyme synthesised.

25 minutes: lysis of cell and release of new phages.

Figure 3.6 Replication cycle in Phage T4

Importance: major tool for genetic and microbiological research.

Relatives: T-even phages all have replication cycles as shown. Some phages, such as bacteriophage lambda, have a *lysogenic* cycle, similar to latency in *Herpes simplex*: the DNA is incorporated into the bacterial chromosome and is replicated with it when the host cell divides. Eventually the latent phage DNA is activated, new phage particles are synthesised and the host cell is lysed. (In any population of bacteria infected in this way, a small proportion are always undergoing lysis, producing new infectious phage.) This property has made bacteriophages useful as vectors in genetic engineering (see Chapter 9, page 80).

CHAPTER 4

MICROBIAL METABOLISM

The basic principles of metabolism are the same for microorganisms as for higher organisms, and are not dealt with from scratch here: these ideas include, for example, the reliance on enzymes to catalyse and control metabolic reactions, the sequencing of reactions in metabolic pathways, the balance between anabolism (building-up reactions) and catabolism (breaking-down reactions), and the use of adenosine triphosphate (ATP) as the cell's universal energy currency. You should also be familiar, in outline at least, with the main stages of respiration (glycolysis, the tricarboxylic acid (Krebs) cycle, and the electron transport chain) and of photosynthesis in higher plants (light-dependent and light-independent stages). If you are uncertain of these, refer to *Biology Advanced Studies - Biochemistry*.

■ CARBON METABOLISM AND THE SYNTHESIS OF ATP

You are probably aware already of the distinction between **autotrophs** and **heterotrophs**. Autotrophs can reduce (fix) inorganic carbon dioxide to organic compounds such as carbohydrates, and use these to synthesise all their other carbon compounds; heterotrophs, on the other hand, must take in their organic compounds ready-made. Among higher organisms, plants are autotrophs, animals including ourselves, heterotrophs.

Both types of metabolism are found among microorganisms, but with more variations. Some microorganisms are **photoautotrophs**, like plants, using sunlight as the source of energy for ATP synthesis and carbon dioxide fixation. Other autotrophic microorganisms, however, obtain energy for ATP synthesis by oxidising inorganic substances: these are the **chemoautotrophs**. Most heterotrophic microorganisms, like animals, are **chemoheterotrophs**, using the organic compounds they take in not only for the synthesis of their own carbon compounds but also as their sole energy source. A few are **photoheterotrophs**, still requiring organic compounds for synthesis but able to use light energy for ATP production.

■ Photoautotrophs

Several different groups of microorganisms can carry out photosynthesis, but they differ in the pigments they use to absorb light energy, and in the sources of hydrogen they use for reduction of carbon dioxide. Table 4.1 summarises the main groups of photoautrotrophic microorganisms. Among the prokaryotes, the green and purple **photosynthetic bacteria** contain *bacteriochlorophylls*, which are chemically slightly different from the chlorophylls of algae and higher plants: they also differ in that they never use water as the source of hydrogen for carbon dioxide reduction, and therefore do not release oxygen as a waste product. **Cyanobacteria** contain chlorophyll a, and therefore use water and release oxygen, but their accessory pigments (phycobilins) are not found in higher plants. The eukaryotic **Chlorophyta** carry out photosynthesis exactly as in C3 plants: in fact, the biochemistry of the light-independent stage of photosynthesis was first worked out using *Chlorella* as the experimental organism.

■ Chemoautotrophs

Chemoautotrophy is found only among bacteria. In all cases, ATP is synthesised from ADP and phosphate using energy obtained by oxidising an inorganic substance (the substrate, or electron donor). The electrons removed from the substrate during its oxidation are transferred to an oxidising agent (or electron acceptor), as shown in Fig. 4.1.

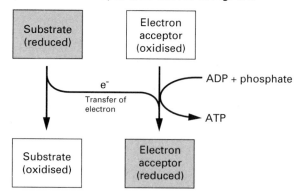

Figure 4.1 ATP production in chemoautotrophs

Group	Light-absorbing pigments	Hydrogen source for CO_2 reduction	Notes
Prokaryotes			
Purple bacteria e.g. *Rhodospirillum*	Bacteriochlorophyll *a* Bacteriochlorophyll *b* Carotenoids Pigments are borne on membranes called **chromatophores**, created by infoldings of plasma membrane	Hydrogen sulphide, H_2S	Use of hydrogen sulphide as hydrogen donor leads to production of sulphur: $CO_2 + 2H_2S \rightarrow (CH_2O) + H_2O + 2S$ (carbohydrate) The sulphur may be stored as globules in the cell. In the absence of hydrogen sulphide it can be used for further CO_2 reduction, producing sulphate ions: $3CO_2 + 2S + 5H_2O \rightarrow (CH_2O) + 4H^+ + 2SO_4^{2-}$
Green bacteria e.g. *Chlorobium*	Bacteriochlorophyll *a* Bacteriochlorophyll *c* (also called *Chlorobium* chlorophyll) Carotenoids Chromatophores apparently independent of plasma membrane.	Hydrogen sulphide, H_2S Thiosulphate ions	Chemistry of carbon dioxide fixation similar to purple bacteria.
Cyanobacteria e.g. *Anabaena* *Nostoc* *Spirulina*	Chlorophyll *a* Carotenoids Phycobilins Most light initially absorbed by phycobilins, present in granules on thylakoid-like membranes: energy passed on to chlorophyll molecules within membranes, where light-dependent stage takes place.	Water	Chemistry of carbon dioxide fixation similar to that in higher plants: oxygen liberated as waste product of light-dependent stage.
Eukaryotes			
Chlorophyta e.g. *Chlorella*	Chlorophyll *a* Chlorophyll *b* Carotenoids	Water	Chemistry of light-dependent and light-independent stages identical to that in higher plants: oxygen liberated as waste product of light-dependent stage.

Table 4.1 Summary of photoautotrophic microorganisms

Organism	Substrate (electron donor)	Oxidising agent (electron acceptor)	Products of reaction	
			from substrate	from oxidising agent
Hydrogenomonas	Hydrogen	Oxygen	Water	Water
Desulphovibrio	Hydrogen	Sulphate ions	Water	Hydrogen sulphide
Beggiatoa	Hydrogen sulphide	Oxygen	Sulphur	Water
Nitrosomonas	Ammonia	Oxygen	Nitrite ions	Water
Nitrobacter	Nitrite ions	Oxygen	Nitrate ions	Water
Thiobacillus denitrificans	Sulphur	Nitrate	Sulphate	Nitrogen
Thiobacillus ferrooxidans	Iron (II) ions	Oxygen	Iron (III) ions	Water

Table 4.2 Chemoautotrophic bacteria

The ATP produced is used in the fixation of carbon dioxide, as it is in photoautotrophs, so no organic carbon source is needed.

Some examples of chemoautotrophic bacteria are shown in Table 4.2. The list includes some ecologically important organisms. *Nitrosomonas* and *Nitrobacter* are important in soil as **nitrifying bacteria**, between them converting ammonia (released by saprophytic decay of proteins) into nitrate, which higher plants are better able to absorb. On the debit side, in poorly aerated soils *Thiobacillus denitrificans* uses nitrate as its electron acceptor, obtaining energy by oxidising sulphur or sulphur compounds to sulphate, and releasing nitrogen as a waste product. It is therefore one of the **denitrifying bacteria**, reducing the nitrate content (and thus the fertility) of soil.

Thiobacillus ferrooxidans has an important biotechnological application, in the extraction of copper from low-grade copper ores.

■ Photoheterotrophs

Not all organisms that can synthesise ATP using energy from sunlight are photosynthetic. *Halobacterium halobium* is a bacterial species found in salty aquatic habitats. When well fed and well oxygenated it is colourless, but when it is grown in a low-oxygen environment it develops purple patches on its plasma membrane (Fig. 4.2). The purple colour is due to *bacteriorhodopsin*, a pigment similar to the rhodopsin found in mammalian rod cells. In *Halobacterium*, however, the pigment is used not for light detection but to generate a proton (hydrogen ion) gradient across the plasma membrane, which is used as an energy source for ATP synthesis. *Halobacterium* is incapable of fixing carbon dioxide, and requires organic compounds from its environment for synthesis of its own carbon compounds. It is not, therefore, autotrophic, and is described as a photoheterotroph.

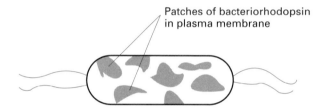

Patches of bacteriorhodopsin in plasma membrane

Figure 4.2 *Halobacterium halogenes* in a low-oxygen environment

Q Why does *Halobacterium* produce its purple patches only in low-oxygen conditions?

■ Chemoheterotrophs

Most microorganisms, prokaryotic and eukaryotic, are chemoheterotrophs: that is, like you and me they rely entirely on the intake of ready-made organic molecules for their energy source and for the synthesis of their carbon compounds. There is, however, enormous variation in the range of organic compounds required: some can be grown in a medium containing a single sugar as the only carbon source, synthesising all of their other organic compounds for themselves; others require a very wide range of organic materials to be provided by the environment, including most or all of the amino acids and often a range of specific growth factors.

■ Respiration

The processes by which energy in organic food molecules is transferred into ATP go under the general name of **respiration**. (It is important to realise that respiration is *not* confined to heterotrophs: autotrophs, whether plants or microorganisms, carry out the process too, to make use of the energy in the organic molecules they have synthesised.) Among microorganisms, three distinct kinds of respiration can be identified:

• aerobic respiration
• anaerobic respiration
• fermentation.

Aerobic respiration in microorganisms does not differ in any important way from the equivalent process in higher organisms such as ourselves: glycolysis (which is anaerobic), the tricarboxylic acid cycle and the electron transport chain all occur in microorganisms, though the electron transport chain is shorter in bacteria, with fewer phosphorylations of ADP per pair of electrons transferred.

Q How does the location of the tricarboxylic acid cycle and the electron transport chain in bacteria differ from its location in eukaryotic cells?

The terms **anaerobic respiration** and **fermentation** are often used as though they mean the same thing. Strictly, they do not. Anaerobic respiration refers to energy-yielding oxidation of organic molecules *using an inorganic substance other than oxygen as the terminal electron acceptor.* For example, in poorly oxygenated soils a number of heterotrophic *denitrifying bacteria* are able to switch from using oxygen to using nitrate ions as their terminal electron acceptor, producing nitrogen gas as a waste product:

$2NO_3 + 5NAD2H + 2H^+ \rightarrow N_2 + 6H_2O + 5NAD$

Pseudomonas denitrificans is an example. Some *Bacillus* species go further still, reducing nitrate ions to ammonia. In fermentation, by contrast, the electron donor and the electron acceptor are both organic, and usually both are produced from the same substrate during its respiration (Fig. 4.3).

At the end of the process, the reduced electron acceptor has no further function in the cell and is excreted. This makes industrially managed fermentations important to humans as the source of many useful chemical products. Table 4.3 summarises a number of important fermentations.

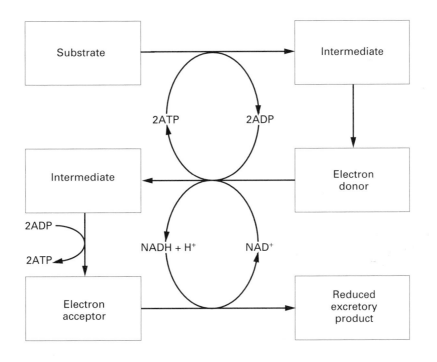

Figure 4.3 Generalised scheme of fermentation

Type of fermentation	Major products	Organisms concerned
Alcoholic	Ethanol Carbon dioxide	Yeasts such as *Saccharomyces* Rarely bacteria
Homolactic	Lactic acid	Bacteria such as *Lactobacillus bulgaricus* and *Streptococcus thermophile*. Some protozoa and fungi
Heterolactic	Lactic acid Ethanol Carbon dioxide	Certain bacteria, e.g. *Leuconostoc*
Propionic	Propionic acid Acetic acid Carbon dioxide	*Propionibacterium* *Clostridium propionicum*
Butyric	Butanol Acetic acid Acetone *or* isopropanol	Various *Clostridium* species: exact combination of end products varies from species to species

Table 4.3 A variety of microbial fermentations

■ NITROGEN METABOLISM

Like animals and plants, all microorganisms require a source of nitrogen from their environment for the synthesis of their amino acids, proteins, nucleotides and other compounds, but there is great variation in the nature of the nitrogen source that can be used (Table 4.4). Some resemble animals like ourselves in requiring organic nitrogen sources such as ready-made amino acids: the number required may range from one or two to the entire set. Many microorganisms resemble plants in being able to assimilate inorganic compounds such as nitrates, using reduced coenzymes from respiratory pathways to reduce them to ammonia, and combining this with organic acids from the TCA cycle (see *Biology Advanced Studies - Biochemistry*) to make amino acids. Only a few are able to use atmospheric nitrogen, reducing it to ammonia and incorporating it directly into amino acids. This unique process, confined to a few specialised prokaryotes, is called nitrogen fixation.

■ Nitrogen fixation

A small number of species of bacteria and cyanobacteria possess a complex enzyme called *nitrogenase*, which catalyses the reduction of nitrogen gas, (N_2), to ammonia: $N_2 + 6[H] \rightarrow 2NH_3$ The ammonia is immediately combined with organic acids in the cell to produce amino acids. The hydrogen for the reduction comes from reduced coenzymes, produced either during respiration or (in the cyanobacteria) in the light-dependent stage of photosynthesis. The reaction is heavily endothermic, the energy coming from hydrolysis of ATP to ADP and phosphate.

Nitrogen fixation is enormously expensive in terms of energy. It is estimated that reduction of a single nitrogen molecule 'costs' the microorganisms between 25 and 35 ATP molecules. This has a number of consequences.

• It is not a process that microorganisms can afford to carry out continuously, whether or not they need it. If other nitrogen sources are available, nitrogen fixation is 'switched off': for example, it can be shown that if ammonia is added to a culture of nitrogen-fixing organisms, nitrogenase synthesis quickly stops.

Q Suggest a mechanism by which this control of nitrogenase synthesis might be exerted.

• There is great selective advantage for heterotrophic nitrogen fixers in forming symbiotic partnerships with plants. The nitrogen fixers have

Minimum nitrogen requirement from environment	Types of microorganism
1. Atmospheric nitrogen	Nitrogen fixers only
2. Nitrates or ammonia	Most autotrophs; many heterotrophic fungi and bacteria
3. One or two specific amino acids	Organisms deficient in one or two specific enzymes involved in amino acid synthesis
4. All amino acids and nitrogenous bases	Obligate parasites; saprophytes exploiting rich organic substrates
(There are many intermediate cases between 3 and 4)	

Table 4.4. Nitrogen requirements of microorganisms

the ability to fix nitrogen, but may lack the energy sources to produce enough ATP for the process; plants, on the other hand, cannot fix nitrogen, but produce abundant energy-rich carbohydrate by photosynthesis. The best-known of these relationships is between plants of the family Papilionaceae (Leguminosae) and bacteria of the genus *Rhizobium* (see the organism file on page 30).

As well as symbionts like *Rhizobium*, nitrogen fixers include a number of free-living bacteria such as *Azotobacter*, *Clostridium* and *Klebsiella*, and cyanobacteria such as *Anabaena*. The nitrogenase enzyme produced is similar in all cases, as is the cluster of genes (the *nif* cluster) concerned with its production. The *nif* genes have been the subject of intensive study, with a view to transferring them by genetic engineering techniques into the cells of crop plants such as wheat.

Q What advantage might be gained by genetically engineering the *nif* genes into plants such as wheat?

Nitrogenase is a complex enzyme, containing iron and molybdenum. All nitrogenases are irreversibly denatured by oxygen. Nitrogen-fixing microorganisms must therefore either live anaerobically, as does *Clostridium*, or must possess some means of protecting their nitrogenase from the air. *Rhizobium* protects its nitrogenase using leghaemoglobin (see the organism file), which binds oxygen to itself. Filamentous cyanobacteria such as *Anabaena* keep their nitrogenase in special thick-walled cells called

heterocysts (see Fig. 1.8): these cells lack the photosynthetic system that splits water, and so do not produce oxygen.

■ BIOSYNTHESIS

Collectively, microorganisms are able to synthesise a huge variety of organic molecules, from an equally large range of starting materials. This is an ability exploited by humans in both ancient and modern biotechnological processes. A complete survey of the synthetic products of microorganisms is outside the scope of this book, but a number of them are considered in Chapter 9. In considering the products of microbial metabolism, we distinguish between **primary metabolites** and **secondary metabolites**.

Primary metabolites are substances made by microorganisms as a result of metabolic processes necessary for the cell's immediate survival. The various fermentation products listed in Table 4.3 are primary metabolites, as they are the products of cell respiration, without which the organisms concerned would quickly die. Secondary metabolites, on the other hand, are the products of metabolic processes which are not essential for the cell's immediate survival (although, of course, they generally contribute to the longer-term fitness of the organism: if they did not, natural selection would quickly alter or eliminate them). The various *antibiotics* secreted by moulds and actinomycete bacteria are good examples of secondary metabolites. These compounds are not necessary to keep the organisms concerned alive, nor are the metabolic pathways leading to them, so if they stopped synthesising them they would not immediately die; instead, antibiotics contribute to the longer-term success of the organisms that make them by reducing local competition from other microorganisms.

The distinction between primary and secondary metabolites is not just an academic one. Because of the contrasting roles they play in the lives of the organisms that synthesise them, their maximum rates of synthesis occur at different times in the organisms' growth cycles. Maximum rates of synthesis of primary metabolites occur when the cells that make them are themselves growing at

their fastest rate; secondary metabolites are more likely to be produced at their highest rates after growth has slowed down. This has obvious implications for the management of microbial growth for production of such metabolites on an industrial scale. If a primary metabolite is being harvested industrially, it will pay to keep the producer organisms growing at their maximum rate indefinitely in *continuous culture*; on the other hand, if a secondary metabolite such as an antibiotic is being harvested, it may be necessary to let a colony of the organism reach maximum size and stop growing before the metabolite is produced in large amounts (*batch culture*).

ORGANISM FILE: *Rhizobium trifolii*

Description: Gram-negative rod-shaped bacterium.
Habitat: soil; forms symbiotic association with root parenchyma cells of clover plants, in swellings of root cortex called *nodules*.

Rhizobium enters clover roots by way of the root hairs. Entry is triggered by interaction of specific glycoproteins on the bacterial cell surface and similar recognition compounds called *lectins* on the root surface. This leads to the root hair *invaginating* (growing back into itself, like the finger of a glove being turned inside-out). The bacteria enter the invagination, which forms an *infection thread* extending all the way to the root cortex.

Once in the root cortext cells, the bacteria divide rapidly, also stimulating the root cells to divide and form the nodule. The bacteria lose their cell walls, becoming surrounded instead by membranes from the host cell: they are now called *bacteroids*, and it is in this form that they fix nitrogen in the root. About half of the mass of a root nodule consists of bacteroids.

Rhizobium bacteroids in bean roots

 What do the two partners in this symbiotic association gain from the partnership?

Rhizobium also induces the host cells to produce a haemoglobin-like molecule, leghaemoglobin. This surrounds the bacteroids and protects their nitrogenase by binding oxygen, which would denature the enzyme. The pink appearance of the leghaemoglobin can be seen if a root nodule is cut open.

Importance: the presence of *Rhizobium* in root nodules of leguminous plants means that they can grow in nitrate-deficient soils where other higher plants may be excluded. When the plants die, the decomposition of their remains returns more fixed nitrogen (nitrates and ammonia) to the soil than they took out during life. This has been used for centuries in clover pastures, and in crop rotations involving leguminous crops such as beans.
Relatives: most leguminous plant species have their own *Rhizobium* species which form symbiotic associations with their roots.

 Why is this high degree of specificity important for the host plant?

CHAPTER 5
THE GROWTH OF MICROORGANISMS

When studying higher organisms like animals and plants, a clear distinction is kept between growth (an irreversible increase in size of individual organisms, as the result of synthesis of new living material) and population increase through reproduction. Applied to microorganisms, however, use of the term growth is less exact, particularly when considering unicells such as bacteria. Growth in such organisms must involve increase in cell size, through synthesis of new cytoplasm and other cell components; but when we talk of 'growing bacteria', we are usually referring to growing *populations* or *colonies* of bacteria, with cells growing in size, then dividing, then growing in size again, and so on. In other words, increases in cell size and in cell numbers are regarded as two aspects of the same overall process.

Bacterial cell division involves replication of genetic material (chromosome and plasmids), followed by the laying down of new cell membranes and wall across the equator of the cell (Fig. 5.1).

How long the process takes depends on the species and the conditions in which growth is taking place (see below). For *Escherichia coli* in optimum conditions, the time between divisions (generation time) can be as little as 20 minutes. In the Protoctista, cell division follows nuclear division by mitosis, and the interval between divisions is generally longer. Minimum generation times of some of the microorganisms described in this book, all growing under their

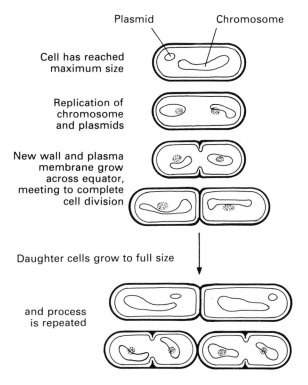

Figure 5.1 Cell growth and division in bacteria

optimum conditions, are given in Table 5.1. (Calculation of generation time is described on page 41.)

Species	Generation time in optimum conditions
Prokaryotes:	
Escherichia coli	20 minutes
Mycobacterium tuberculosis	18 hours
Anabaena cylindrica	24 hours
Eukaryotes:	
Amoeba proteus	24 hours
Saccharomyces cerevisiae	2 hours

Table 5.1 Generation times of some representative microorganisms

■ FACTORS AFFECTING MICROBIAL GROWTH

A number of environmental factors affect the rate at which microorganisms grow and reproduce. Among the most important are the following.

Nutrients
For growth to occur, the environment must provide:
- **water;**
- a suitable **carbon source** –
  for autotrophs, carbon dioxide;
  for heterotrophs, all organic compounds that cannot be synthesised within the cell.
  The minimum for heterotrophs with limited synthetic capability is a wide range including numerous *growth factors* (usually molecules such as thiamine, riboflavine and biotin that act as coenzymes);
- a suitable **nitrogen source** –
  usually nitrate or ammonia (for nitrogen-fixing prokaryotes, nitrogen gas can be used instead). For heterotrophs with limited synthetic capability, amino acids (from one to the entire range) are needed;
- all **mineral ions** needed as enzyme cofactors and as components of other molecules.

A suitable pH
Many microorganisms can grow at any pH between 6 and 9. Fungi may grow well much below pH 6 but only specialised acid-tolerant species of bacteria (such as *Lactobacillus*) will do so; at the other extreme, specialised decomposers of urea (such as the bacterium *Sporosarcina ureae*) tolerate pH values well above 9, and cannot grow below pH 8.

Q Suggest why urea decomposers are adapted to live at high pH.

Extremes of pH affect the growth of microorganisms mainly by the effect they have on the structure of proteins, especially enzymes. The membranes of microbial cells are not very permeable to hydrogen ions or hydroxyl ions so the effects of acids and alkalis on microbial growth are exerted mainly by undissociated molecules entering the cell.

Oxygen
Obligate aerobes such as *Mycobacterium* will grow only in the presence of abundant free oxygen.

Microaerophiles (including many gut bacteria) grow best at low oxygen concentrations and are inhibited at 20% oxygen (atmospheric concentration).

Facultative anaerobes such as baker's yeast will grow in the absence of oxygen, but more slowly than if oxygen were present. (See page 47.)

Obligate anaerobes such as *Clostridium* will grow only in the absence of oxygen, which is toxic to them.

Temperature
Most microorganisms are **mesophilic**, growing best at temperatures between 20 °C and 45 °C. Organisms growing best at temperatures below 20 °C are described as **psychrophilic**; those which grow best at temperatures above 45 °C are **thermophilic**. Marine and soil organisms are often psychrophilic, whilst thermophiles are found in habitats such as hot springs.

Temperature affects microbial growth through its effects on enzyme activity. Low temperatures reduce the frequency of enzyme-substrate collisions, whilst high temperatures alter the tertiary structure of enzyme molecules and may denature them. Fig. 5.2 shows the influence of temperature on the growth rate of *Escherichia coli*.

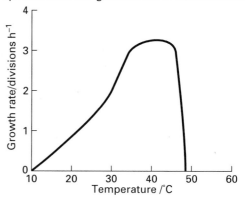

Figure 5.2 Effect of temperature on maximum growth rate of *Escherichia*

Q How does the curve in Fig. 5.2 compare with the typical graph of enzyme activity against temperature?

Light
Exposure to light is obviously essential for photoautotrophic species. Its effect on growth depends on how close its intensity is to the limiting value: above this intensity, other factors (such as temperature or carbon dioxide concentration) are more likely to determine the growth rate. As well as intensity, the quality (wavelength) of light may be important in determining growth rate: for example, the phycobilins of cyanobacteria absorb best in the blue end of the spectrum, these being the wavelengths that best penetrate water.

LABORATORY CULTURE OF MICROORGANISMS

Note: the types of procedure described in this section are suitable for schools unless otherwise indicated, but safety procedures described are *not* exhaustive. For further guidance, see *'Microbiology: An HMI Guide for Schools and Non-advanced Further Education'* (HMSO 1990).

The following basic principles apply when growing microorganisms in the laboratory.
• The organisms are grown, when possible, in artificial **culture media**. (Viruses cannot be grown in artificial media, nor can some bacteria and fungi that are obligate parasites: these organisms must be cultured in living cells.)
• The organisms are grown under **controlled conditions**. In particular, the culture is **incubated** at a known temperature, and the **pH** of the medium is known and often controlled using buffers.
• Microorganisms are almost always grown in **pure (axenic) culture** – that is, in populations consisting of only one species. (This might not be so if a microbiologist is studying the interaction of two or more populations with each other, or if the organism being grown requires another as food, as might be the case with some protozoa.) To obtain pure cultures microbiologists need methods for **isolating** organisms from the mixed communities that exist in nature. To keep the cultures pure, and to prevent the escape of possibly dangerous organisms from culture, they need to practise **aseptic technique**.

Culture media

For general use in isolating and growing microorganisms, fairly crude media may be used. These may be based on meat extract, blood, milk, yeast extract, or other nutrient-rich sources, and will usually contain a wide range of nutrients such as sugars, amino acids and vitamins. **Nutrient broth** and **nutrient agar** are good examples.

For more detailed study of microbial growth and metabolism, microbiologists usually use synthetic media of precisely known composition. This has numerous advantages.
• The contents of synthetic culture media are known and controlled, so valid comparisons can be made between the growth of different species, or of the same species under different conditions.
• Biochemists studying metabolic pathways in microorganisms can use **minimal** media to supply or withhold specific nutrients and observe the effects. A minimal medium, as the name suggests, is one which provides the bare minimum of nutrients required by the species under investigation. For many heterotrophs, this may consist of the necessary mineral ions, with perhaps a single sugar as the only carbon and energy source. In this way, we can quickly establish which sugars a particular organism can and cannot metabolise. Other types may not grow in a minimal medium unless specific amino acids or growth factors are added, thus giving important information about their abilities to synthesise.
• The nutrient content of the medium, and its pH, can be adjusted to favour the growth of the particular organism being studied and exclude others. Media like this are called **selective** or **narrow-spectrum** media.

Either solid or liquid media may be used for growing microorganisms, depending on the purpose of the investigation. Solid media are usually based on **agar**, a seaweed extract containing polysaccharides. Nutrients are added to molten agar, and the mixture sets into a jelly on which microorganisms can grow. Because most microorganisms are unable to digest agar, it remains solid even when they are growing on the nutrients it contains. One of the advantages of growing organisms on agar media is that they grow as separate visible **colonies**, each colony consisting of the offspring of a single organism. This is important in the isolation of microorganisms from mixed cultures, and also in their identification, as colonies of different species often differ in size, shape and colour. Fig. 5.3 shows some of the different forms bacterial colonies can take.

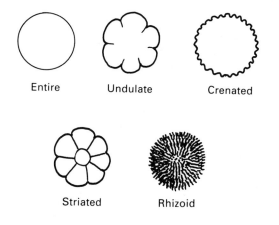

Entire   Undulate   Crenated

Striated   Rhizoid

Figure 5.3 Some bacterial colony forms in surface view

Sterilisation

Practical microbiology requires sterile equipment. Where possible, the preferred method of sterilisation is **autoclaving**. An autoclave is a sealed container in which apparatus is heated at 121 °C in steam at a pressure of 103 kN m^{-2} (15 lb in^{-2}). To be certain of sterility, this temperature and pressure must be maintained for at least 15 minutes after full pressure has been reached.

The working surface must also be sterilised by wiping with strong disinfectant: this should be done before and after practical procedures.

Pouring plates

Solid media are usually used in Petri dishes. The medium is made up in liquid form, and may be dispensed into small screw-top bottles before being autoclaved. After autoclaving, the medium can be kept liquid until required by placing the bottle in a water bath at 60 °C. Petri dishes may be glass (also sterilised by autoclaving), or the disposable plastic variety supplied in packs which are sterile until opened.

Before pouring the plate, the agar should be cooled to 50-55 °C. To avoid contamination, the plate should be poured quickly with the lid of the Petri dish held ajar. While the agar in the dish is still hot, the lid may safely be left ajar as the outflow of steam will prevent airborne organisms from entering. This helps to reduce problems of condensation on the Petri dish lid. After cooling and setting of the gel, the closed dish is kept upside down. If condensation is still a problem, the dish can be kept overnight in a warm incubator to remove excess moisture.

Culture vessels for liquid media

Virtually any piece of glassware that can be sterilised and plugged can be used for growing microorganisms, but for serious study a **fermenter** or **bioreactor** of some kind is commonly used. A typical example is shown in Fig. 5.4.

As you can see, a fermenter of this kind has a number of advantages over a plain culture tube or bottle.

• Air can be passed in and out through lines fitted with filters: this provides oxygen for aerobes, and also stirs the culture, improving contact between microorganisms and nutrients. A sparger on the air inlet produces a large number of very tiny bubbles, increasing the total surface area of air in contact with water and thus the rate of entry of oxygen into solution.

• If needed, a magnetic stirrer can be used as well, further improving mixing of the culture.

• Syringes can be fitted for inoculation of the medium with microorganisms, for the addition of materials during the growth of the culture, or for the taking of samples for analysis or population estimation.

In addition, the culture vessel is usually maintained at constant temperature, either in an incubator or in a thermostatically controlled water bath.

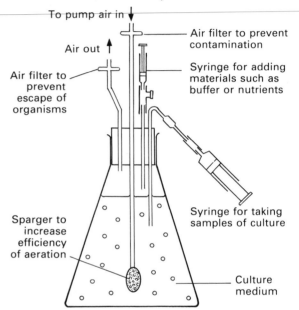

Figure 5.4 A simple fermenter suitable for school use

Continuous and batch culture

The fermenter in Fig. 5.4 is set up for a *batch culture*: that is, it is ready to be inoculated with a culture of microorganisms, which will multiply, changing the conditions in the medium by using up the nutrients and producing their own waste products. Eventually conditions in the culture will become too unfavourable for the organisms to survive, and the population will die out. Batch culture is suitable for most school-based experiments on microbial growth, and is used industrially in many processes that harvest the secondary metabolites of microorganisms as their products. Secondary metabolites are produced by metabolic processes which are not essential to the organism's short-term survival (see page 29), and are often not produced in large amounts when the organism is growing at its fastest rate; industrial production is therefore most efficient if the organisms are allowed to reach maximum population size and stop growing before the product is harvested.

Continuous culture, by contrast, aims to keep a culture growing indefinitely. This can be done if:

- fresh nutrients are continually supplied
- accumulated cells and waste products are removed at the same rate
- conditions such as temperature and pH are kept at their optimum values.

A culture vessel designed for continuous culture is called a **chemostat**. Fig. 5.5 shows an example of a suitable device. In addition to the features shown, the culture vessel would probably be fitted with temperature and pH probes for monitoring growth conditions.

Continuous culture is important in industrial processes that harvest the primary metabolites of microorganisms as their products. (Primary metabolites are produced in greatest quantities when the organisms are growing at their fastest rate: see page 29.)

■ Inoculating media with microorganisms

Growing microorganisms in the laboratory usually involves transferring them from an existing pure culture onto fresh medium (*subculturing* them), or isolating them from some natural source. The process of introducing microorganisms into an new medium is called *inoculation*, and is usually done with a wire loop or a sterile pipette (often a *Pasteur pipette*, with its end drawn out into a fine taper).

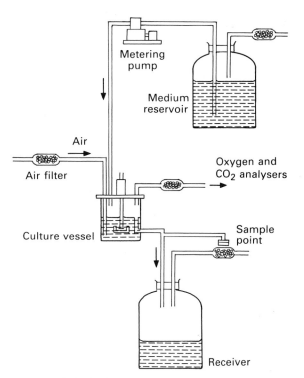

Figure 5.5 A simple chemostat

Fig. 5.6 shows a suitable aseptic procedure for inoculating a sterile agar plate with organisms from a pure or mixed liquid culture.

1. Sterilise wire loop in bunsen flame.

2. Remove plug from source culture and pass neck of tube through bunsen flame 2 or 3 times.

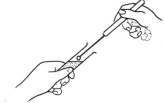

3. Use loop to take sample of source culture.

4. Re-flame neck of tube and replace plug.

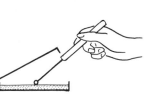

5. Inoculate plate.

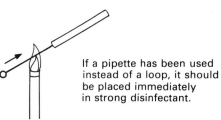

If a pipette has been used instead of a loop, it should be placed immediately in strong disinfectant.

6. Re-sterilise loop by heating shaft first, then slowly drawing loop through flame. This avoids explosive 'sputtering' of drops of culture, which may fling organisms clear of the flame before they have been killed.

Figure 5.6 Aseptic technique: using a wire loop to inoculate an agar plate

■ Incubating cultures

After inoculation, the lid of the Petri dish should be taped onto the base using two strips of adhesive tape, crossed over (Fig. 5.7). It should not be completely sealed, as this would encourage the growth of anaerobic pathogens such as *Clostridium*. The dish should be clearly labelled with wax pencil, on the base rather than the lid.

Professional microbiologists usually incubate their cultures at the optimum temperature for growth of the organism concerned. In schools, however, incubation should not be carried out above 30°C, to avoid favouring the growth of human pathogens.

■ Disposal of cultures

After examination, cultures should be sterilised before disposal. This is best done in autoclavable plastic bags. After autoclaving, disposable materials such as plastic Petri dishes can be sealed inside the bags and placed in a dustbin.

■ Isolating methods

Note: subculturing organisms from the wild is not a recommended procedure for schools.

Individual species can be isolated by spreading a mixed culture so thinly on a plate of solid medium that individual cells are separated and will grow into separate colonies. This may be done in one of two ways.

1. A sterile Pasteur pipette is used to place a very small drop of the mixed culture on the plate, and a sterile glass spreader (a glass rod bent at a right angle) used to spread the drop very thinly over the surface of the medium.
2. A wire loop is used to make two or three streaks of mixed culture near the edge of an agar plate. The loop is sterilised in a bunsen flame, then streaked two or three more times at an angle across the previous streaks. This is repeated several times (see Fig. 5.8).

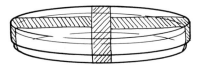

Figure 5.7 A Petri dish sealed after inoculation

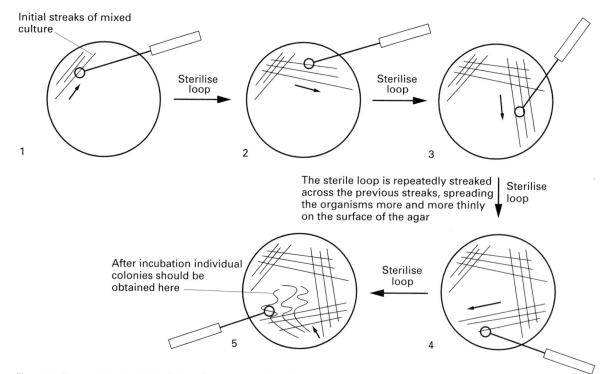

Figure 5.8 The streak method for isolating microorganisms from mixed culture

When clearly separate colonies have been obtained, it is safe to assume that each is the product of a single cell. A pure culture of the organism concerned can be obtained by picking a sample of the colony off the plate with a sterile loop and streaking it onto a fresh sterile plate or re-suspending it in sterile liquid medium.

■ Measurement of growth

The size of a microbial population in liquid culture may be measured by counting cells directly, or by taking some indirect measure such as the turbidity (cloudiness) of the culture. Direct cell counts may be divided into total counts, which include both living and dead cells, and viable counts, which count living cells only.

■ Counting cells

In practice, it is never possible to count whole populations of microorganisms: instead, the cells in a very small measured sample of a culture are counted, and the result multiplied up to give a population density in organisms per cm³ of culture. Even then, the population density is likely to be so high that cell counts are usually made in known *dilutions* of the culture.

Dilutions are made *serially*: if 1 cm³ of a liquid is pipetted into 9 cm³ of sterile saline solution, it has been diluted ×10; if 1 cm³ of this dilution is now pipetted into 9 cm³ of sterile saline solution, the dilution is ×100; and so on, until a countable dilution is reached (Fig. 5.9). When the density of cells in a given dilution has been found, multiplying by the dilution factor gives the density in the original culture.

Q A 10^{-5} dilution of a bacterial culture was found to contain 10^4 cells per cm³. What was the population density of the original culture?

Total counts can be made using a **haemocytometer**. This is a special microscope slide with a very fine grid etched on its central section. A drop of the microbial culture is placed on the grid and a special cover slip suspended above it. The cover slip traps a known depth of liquid (usually 0.1 mm) above the grid: since the dimensions of the grid squares are known, the volume of fluid over each square is easily calculated, and direct counting gives the number of cells in this volume of culture. Fig. 5.10 gives an example.

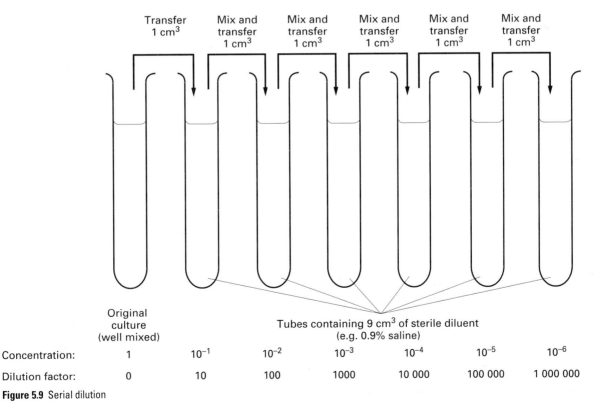

	Transfer 1 cm³	Mix and transfer 1 cm³	Mix and transfer 1 cm³	Mix and transfer 1 cm³	Mix and transfer 1 cm³	Mix and transfer 1 cm³

Original culture (well mixed) — Tubes containing 9 cm³ of sterile diluent (e.g. 0.9% saline)

Concentration:	1	10^{-1}	10^{-2}	10^{-3}	10^{-4}	10^{-5}	10^{-6}
Dilution factor:	0	10	100	1000	10 000	100 000	1 000 000

Figure 5.9 Serial dilution

Cells are counted as being 'in' a square if they do not touch the sides, or if they touch the top or right-hand side. Cells touching the bottom or left-hand sides would be counted in the cells below and to the left respectively.

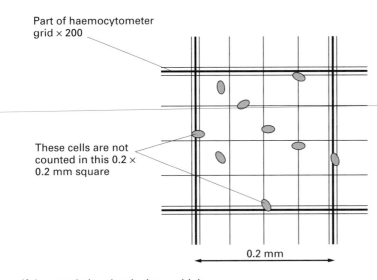

Part of haemocytometer grid × 200

These cells are not counted in this 0.2 × 0.2 mm square

0.2 mm

Number of cells counted in this 0.04 mm^2 square = 7
Depth of liquid under cover slip = 0.1 mm.
If this is a 10^{-5} dilution of the original culture, what is the culture's population density?
Answer:
there are 7 cells in 0.004 mm^3 of 10^{-5} dilution
⟶ there are 7/0.004 = 1750 cells in 1 mm^3 of 10^{-5} dilution
⟶ there are 1750 × 10^5 = 1.75 × 10^8 cells in 1 mm^3 of the original culture.
⟶ there are 1.75 × 10^{10} cells in 1 cm^3 of the original culture.
Population density: 1.75 × 10^{10} cm^{-3}.
(In practice, the average count in many such cells would be taken.)

If the population density is very high, cells may be counted in the small (0.05 × 0.05 mm) squares. With a 0.1 mm depth of fluid, each of these represents a volume of 0.00025 mm^3.

Figure 5.10 Use of a haemocytometer

A 10^{-6} dilution of a bacterial culture is examined in a haemocytometer. One 0.2 × 0.2 mm square of the grid has this appearance (Fig.5.11):

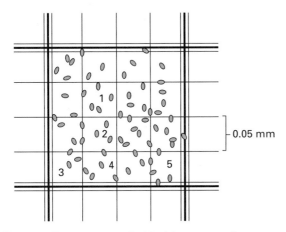

0.05 mm

Figure 5.11 The appearance of a 0.2 × 0.2 mm square of a haemocytometer grid

Counting cells in small (0.05 mm) squares 1, 2, 3, 4 and 5 *only*, what is your estimate of the popula-tion density of the original culture?

One of the limitations of direct counting is that live cells cannot be distinguished from dead ones, and so a misleading impression might be obtained of the *live* population density. A **viable count** of the living population can be made by spreading a small volume (say 0.1 or 0.01 cm^3) of a series of dilutions onto sterile agar plates. Dilutions which are too low (i.e. too concentrated) will give 'carpets' of growth or uncountable numbers of colonies; those so high (dilute) as to give only a few colonies per plate are unreliable (as the chance inclusion of one colony more or less per plate would make a very large difference to the popula-tion estimate). It is hoped that at least one dilution in the series will give a high but countable number of colonies per plate. Since each colony represents one living cell from the original culture, multiply-ing up gives the viable cell count. Fig. 5.12 gives an example.

Q Estimate the population density of the original culture in Fig. 5.12.

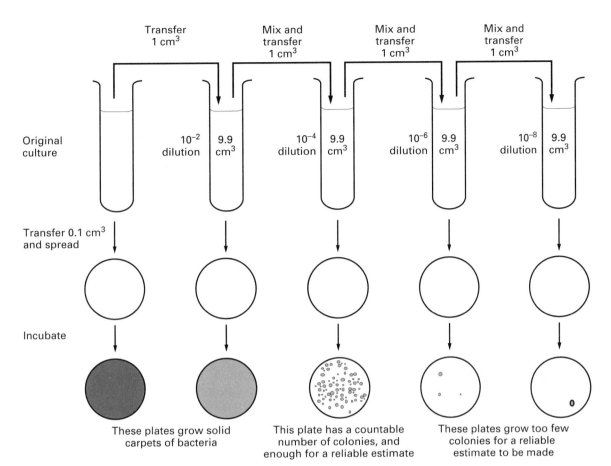

Figure 5.12 Viable counting by dilution plating

■ Turbidity as an indirect measure of microbial growth

The turbidity of a culture is measured by placing a given quantity in a standard glass tube (a *cuvette*) and reading its absorbance in a colorimeter. The colorimeter is set to zero using a cuvette of culture medium only: subsequent absorbance readings above zero are taken as measures of microbial population.

Turbidity readings are, of course, in absorbance units, and give no direct measure of the number or mass of microorganisms in the culture. However, if a liquid culture is inoculated with a microbial population and simultaneously cell counts and turbidity readings are made as the population grows, a calibration curve can be plotted (turbidity reading against number of cells). In future growth experiments using the same organism and the same medium, this curve can be used to convert turbidity readings directly into number of cells. (The curve will not be linear, and is valid only

within the range initially plotted.)

Turbidity readings are quick and easy to take, but as a means of monitoring microbial growth they have a number of limitations.

• They are valid and reliable only with very small cells spread evenly throughout the medium. They cannot be used to measure growth of fungal mycelia, nor of large cells such as protozoa, which are likely to scatter light unevenly.

• Like total cell counts, they do not distinguish between living and dead cells.

• Substances secreted by microorganisms, as well as the chemical components of broken-up cells, will also change the turbidity of the medium, giving a misleading high reading.

Q The methods of measuring microbial growth discussed above have concentrated on cellular organisms growing in liquid culture. How would you measure the growth of a mould on an agar plate?

Robert Koch (1843-1910)

Koch was a German physician who discovered that a specific microorganism was responsible for cattle anthrax – and that it could be grown in culture. Working at the same time as Pasteur, he discovered the way to grow pure cultures and also how to use solid agar and gelatine plates. His work on cholera identified the vibrio bacterium and showed that it was carried in water. This led to the control of a cholera epidemic in Hamburg by the filtration of drinking water. He won a Nobel prize in 1905 for his work on tuberculosis. In spite of all this he is best remembered for his 'rules for microbiology' which are known as Koch's postulates. They can be stated as:

(a) to identify a microorganism as the cause of a disease the microorganism must always be found in animals suffering the disease and not in those not suffering the disease.

(b) the microorganism must be grown in pure culture away from the body of the animal.

(c) when the cultured organism is inoculated into a susceptible animal, the disease symptoms should develop.

(d) when the organism is re-isolated from the diseased animal and cultured, it should be demonstrated to be the same as the original.

■ GROWTH CURVES

If a small number of microorganisms are inoculated into a liquid medium, and the population measured at intervals over a suitable period of time, the figures can be used to plot a growth curve. Because the early readings are relatively small numbers (perhaps hundreds or thousands of cells per cm^3) and later ones very large (tens of millions or hundreds of millions per cm^3) it is virtually impossible to plot them all accurately on a normal arithmetic scale. For this reason, population numbers are almost always plotted as *logarithms*, usually to the base 10. (Any non-zero number can be written as a power of 10: thus $1 = 10^0$, $2 = 10^{0.301}$, $10 = 10^1$, $1000 = 10^3$, and so on. The base-10 logarithm of a number is the power of 10 that the number represents:

$\log_{10} 2 = 0.301$
$\log_{10} 1000 = 3$
$\log_{10} 100\,000\,000 = 8$

If you're still not sure why we use log scales to plot microbial growth curves, try plotting the numbers 2 and 100 000 000 on the same graph axis (i) in their usual (arithmetic) form, and (ii) as their base-10 logarithms. (Logarithms can be found using a pocket calculator by entering the number and then pressing the button marked 'log' or 'log 10^x'; alternatively they can be looked up in log tables.)

■ Phases of growth

When we plot $\log_{10}$ (number of organisms) against time for a growing culture, the resulting curve usually follows a predictable pattern (Fig. 5.13). For a short period immediately after inoculation, the organisms are synthesising the enzymes needed to exploit the new medium, and perhaps growing in size. This is the **lag phase**, during which there is no increase in the number of cells. (If the organisms have been transferred from an identical medium at the same temperature, the lag phase may be very short or non-existent.)

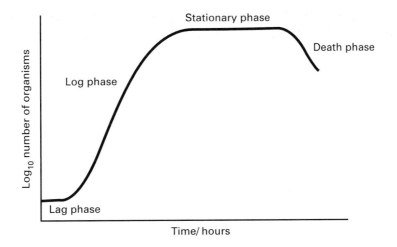

Figure 5.13 Growth curve for a bacterial culture

When reproduction starts, the presence of abundant food, and the absence of competition and of inhibiting factors such as toxic waste products, allows cell division to occur at a high rate. This gives rise to the **log phase** (or **exponential phase**) of population growth, in which the population doubles at regular intervals. Plotted as arithmetic numbers of cells, the log phase would give a curve of ever-increasing gradient; plotted as logs of cell numbers, it gives a straight line.

If you are still uncertain about this try the following exercise. Assume that a bacterium divides every 20 minutes (so starting at 00.00 with one, there would be 2 at 00.20, 4 at 00.40 and 8 at 01.00, etc.). Write down the numbers for each 20 minutes for 8 hours. Now plot this data as arithmetic and logarithmic graphs.

In closed cultures, however, the organisms sooner or later begin to run out of food, and may also be poisoned by their own accumulated wastes. As a result, growth slows down and stops, and the culture enters the **stationary phase**. If population size is being measured by a total cell count, or by turbidity readings, there may be no apparent further change. A viable count, however, will soon show a decline as cells begin to die and the culture enters the **death phase**, continuing until no living cells are left.

■ The growth rate constant

During the log phase, the number of microorganisms in a culture doubles at regular intervals. The time taken for the population to double is called the **generation time**, and the number of generations produced per hour is called the **exponen-**tial growth rate constant, represented as K. The growth rate constant and the generation time for a given culture can be found as follows.

Suppose we make two measurements of population size (N) during the log phase, t hours apart. We will call the first measurement N_0, the second N_t. During time t, there were a certain number of divisions (or generations): call the number of generations n.

Then $$n = \frac{\log_{10} N_t - \log_{10} N_0}{\log_{10} 2}$$

i.e. $$n = \frac{\log_{10} N_t - \log_{10} N_0}{0.301}$$

(You might care to prove this for yourself: start with the fact that $N_t = 2^n \times N_0$. If you are not mathematically inclined, don't worry about where the equation comes from – just accept that it works!)

Once we know that there are n generations in t hours, we can find the growth rate constant K:
K = n/t generations hour^{-1}
We can also find the generation time, which is equal to 1/K hours or 60/K minutes.

Q A student counts the number of bacteria in a liquid culture at 10 am, and again at 3 pm. Her cell counts are as follows:
10 am   25 000 cells cm^{-3}
3 pm   200 000 cells cm^{-3}
Calculate the growth rate constant (K) and the generation time for this culture.

You could now answer the two questions on pages 42 and 43.

Q 1. The graphs below show the growth of cultures of two microorganisms in industrial fermenters and the yield of two of their products. Graph A shows the growth of the yeast *Saccharomyces* and the yield of its product, ethanol. Graph B shows the growth of the ascomycete mould *Penicillium* and the yield of its product, the antibiotic penicillin.

(a) (i) Explain what is happening in the growth of the yeast population as shown in graph A during each of the following time periods:

> 0-2 hours
> 4-6 hours
> 8-10 hours
> 12-14 hours

(ii) Describe the relationship between the growth of the yeast and the yield of ethanol.

(b) (i) State *three* ways in which the pattern of accumulation of penicillin in graph B differs from the pattern of accumulation of ethanol in graph A.

(ii) Ethanol is described as a *primary* metabolite of *Saccharomyces*: it is a direct product of metabolic processes essential for the life of the organism. Penicillin is described as a *secondary* metabolite of

Penicillium: it is a product of metabolic processes which are not essential to keep the organism alive.

Suggest how the differences in the patterns of accumulation of these two products may be related to their differing roles in the metabolism of the producer organisms.

(London, A-Level Biology1992.)

Q 2. The graph on page 43 (Fig. 5.15) shows changes in the number of cells and in the amount of DNA in a culture of yeast over a period of 5 hours. Temperature and pH were maintained at a constant level throughout the investigation.

(a) Outline a method by which the population density of yeast cells in the culture could be determined.

(b) (i) What is the time taken for the population of yeast cells at Time 0 to double?

(ii) How does the doubling time for subsequent generations differ from that of the initial population?

(iii) Suggest an explanation for your answer to (b) (ii).

(c) Describe and explain the relation between the two curves shown on the graph.

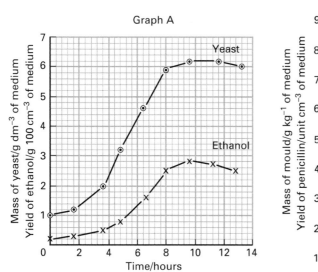

Graph A

Figure 5.14

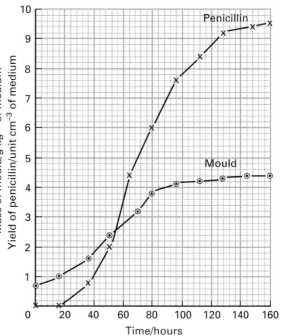

Graph B

Yeast and other microorganisms can be used to produce useful substances. The table shows some aspects of fermentation in a culture of the bacterium *Corynebacterium glutamicum* in producing the amino acid lysine which is used to supplement cereal protein.

Time/ hours	Cell dry mass/g	Lysine/ g dm^{-3}	Residual sugar/%
0	10.0	0.7	20.0
10	12.7	1.1	19.2
20	15.7	9.3	18.2
30	20.1	17.3	13.1
40	24.2	30.2	10.2
50	25.7	40.7	5.4
60	26.0	44.0	2.4
70	26.0	42.1	2.8

Table 5.2

(d) Plot the data *in the first three columns* of the table as a graph. Use a single pair of axes and join the points with straight lines.

(e) (i) Calculate the rate of growth of the bacterial population during the period 20 to 40 hours and during the period 50 to 70 hours. Show your working.
   (ii) Using evidence from these data, suggest *two* possible explanations for the difference in rates of growth of the bacterial population in these two periods.

The diagram shows part of the biochemical pathway by which lysine is synthesised by *C. glutamicum*. Threonine and lysine both inhibit the enzyme which is necessary to convert aspartate to aspartyl phosphate.

(f) (i) Use the material in this diagram to explain what is meant by negative feedback.

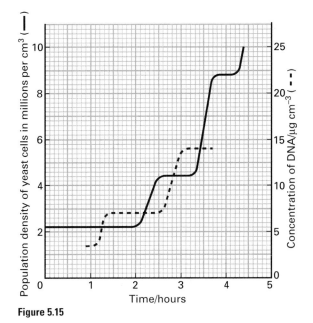

Figure 5.15

(ii) Suggest how a strain of *C. glutamicum* deficient in Enzyme A can give an increased yield of lysine.

(AEB, A-Level Biology 1993.)

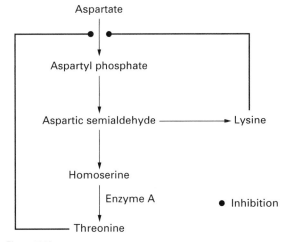

Figure 5.16

CHAPTER 6

BIOTECHNOLOGY - INDUSTRIAL FERMENTATION

■ BOOZE AND BOOZA

Some nomadic Egyptians still follow, in one respect, the way of life developed by their ancestors six thousand years ago. They make bread dough from flour and water and allow the air-borne yeasts to invade this starchy food source and cause the dough to rise. They bake most of it as flat bread but keep some of this old dough to mix in with the freshly prepared dough that they will make the next day. They have evolved a technique of keeping the 'sour dough' with its live yeast by covering it with water. As they start the daily baking process, they pour off the liquid and drink the sour, alcoholic beverage that has developed during the hot day. This drink is known as **booza**. They have used a skill which combines two biotechnologies.

What is biotechnology? Until the mid-1970s the term was hardly known. There was the technology of Industrial Biochemistry and a few techniques of food production. However, with the introduction of new methods of mass cultivation of microbes in the 1940s, and the later development of genetic engineering, scientists realised that this heralded a major area of development of biological science. An article in *The Economist* (1979) stated that the new biotechnology may become 'an industry as characteristic of the twenty-first century as those based on physics and chemistry have been of the twentieth century'. Every month, reports in the scientific journals give us fresh and exciting news of developments, and the newspapers have frequent items about 'super bugs' and 'miracle cures' (and some of it, they even manage to get right).

Q Look out for reports on biotechnology and try to identify misunderstandings or even attempts to confuse the general public.

Kirk Raab (the President of **Genentech**) wrote in 1993 that 'from the cheese we eat that is made with bioengineered rennin to the news reports we hear of criminals convicted based on minute bodily evidence, biotechnology is already a part

Making bread in the desert

of our daily lives'. The main impact has already been in the pharmaceutical industry with the production of proteins such as insulin, growth hormone, antibiotics and vaccines, and chemical tests for genetic and immunological diseases. The links with microbiology are obvious in medicine. In the biotechnology of agriculture, DNA technology, industry and food production, microbes also play their part. The examples that follow help one to start thinking about modern biotechnology.

■ ENZYMES, SCOTTISH CAVIAR AND CIDER

A small trout-farm in Inverawe, Scotland, marketed fresh and smoked trout. The waste trimmings, bones, skin, heads and viscera were ground up and converted to fertilisers. They then discovered that some of the 'waste' internal organs had value as a luxury delicacy. The mature ovaries were full of eggs, and this roe could be marketed as trout caviar. This was a significant financial development but the business really took off when the traditional method of releasing the eggs was replaced by a simple biotechnological technique. The traditional method, still used to produce Russian caviar, is to remove gonads from the freshly killed female fish and rub them through a slotted board. In Scotland this method would have involved high staff costs and would not have been allowed because of hygiene regulations for the handling of a food item.

Biotechnologists came up with a solution: an enzyme was used to remove the connective tissue and release the eggs. This saved time and trouble and conserved more of the precious eggs as well as being highly cost effective. Microbes had produced the enzyme by fermentation. There is more information on this type of enzyme biotechnology later.

This example of the use of microbial enzymes helps us to understand the definition that has been developed for the biotechnology industry. Biotechnology is **'the exploitation of living organisms or biological processes – a set of enabling technologies that can be used profitably in many industrial sectors'** (Department of Trade and Industry).

Trout caviar

Perhaps more people associate biotechnology with fermentation and we shall examine some processes later. However, anyone who has attempted to make wine at home will understand the basic process and know that even after the fruit juices have fermented, a stubborn cloudiness may remain. This is unattractive but can be removed by using a chemical on sale in the High Street chemists. It is called *pectinase* (see photograph) and is an enzyme. It had been used since 1930 without brewers really understanding what was happening. The information given below explains why the enzyme process works. A similar technology was used in 1989 by Merrydown Wines – a major cider manufacturer. They had a production close-down when it was found that their cider started turning cloudy three days after bottling. A simple biotechnology-based system solved the problem and enabled production to resume. So what caused the problem, what did they do about it and and how were enzymes involved?

Cider is still made by traditional means in small quantities on farms in Somerset and Devon. The apples are crushed in a cider-press and the resulting juice filtered and left to ferment for up to eight weeks in unheated barns in winter. The large barrels are tapped to allow sale of a draught cider whose exact content cannot be guaranteed! The commercial industry must be certain of the composition of its products and their cider is fermented in huge tanks holding 1.6 million gallons. The traditional skills of the cider-maker must, to some extent, give way to the more exact methods of the scientist – the industrial biotechnologist.

Bulmer's steel fermentation vats

How much pure, fresh juice could *you* get from an apple? You might think about a technique for chopping and crushing it; perhaps even putting it into a blender and filtering the extract. You would not get a great yield! However if you were to mix a small amount of pectinase with the chopped apple the juice really flows. The enzyme (you should recall that it is a biological catalyst) doesn't get used up – so a little goes a long way! This is what happens. The apple pulp, skin and core are made up of cells held together by a 'glue' of pectin. If this can be removed the cells fall apart. It happens in the natural state when fruit 'goes bad' and softens because of the action of the digestive enzymes (pectinase) produced by microorganisms.

Eventually these enzymes separate the cells and also break down the actual cell wall material to release the cell contents – the fruit juice. By this time though the fruit is usually quite rotten and the juice undrinkable.

In the chopped apple example above the enzyme action takes place at an accelerated pace and the pure fresh apple juice is released. Commercially this can either be put into bottles and cartons as apple juice or fermented to produce cider. World-wide over 3 million tonnes of apples are processed into juice each year. Some of it is sold in a cloudy state but most is clarified.

And how does pectinase clarify apple juice, cider and home-brewed wines? Some of the pectins in fruit are insoluble slimy particles that retain juice and remain in the pulp so that the juice is too viscous to flow. In addition pectins form a protective coat around particles of protein debris in the juice and prevent them from sinking. This causes the cloudiness. When pectinase is added, breakdown of pectin occurs, and the protein particles clump together and become heavy enough to settle out. The juice is then centrifuged and filtered.

Depectinisation can be achieved by a range of naturally occurring pectolytic enzymes. Specific ones have been developed for specific tasks. A fungal enzyme can operate even in the low pH (2.2 - 2.8) of lemon juice and it is only a matter of time before gene technology (see page 77) will allow the production of other enzymes with different pH optima and better heat stability.

And the pectin that we have just been removing and destroying? Well, it is also an important natural product and 'pectin solutions' are produced, often from orange skins, to help jams to gel. Yet another enzyme process; yet another biotechnology.

CASE STUDY

Spray-painted on the wall above the huge fermentation vat was the formula

$$C_6H_{12}O_6 \rightarrow 2CO_2 + 2C_2H_5OH$$

as if to remind the brewery workers that other living organisms were at work forming the product for which the brewery was so famous. The barrels and bottles of beer are the products. The raw materials are the sacks of malted barley and the yeast *Saccharomyces cerevisiae* (see the organism file page 17) as well as a suitable supply of water. Because of the importance of water quality the most famous beers have been brewed in certain areas – Burton-on-Trent, Dublin and Newcastle as well as Munich (Germany) and Plzen in the Czech Republic.

The malted barley is the substrate – it arrives at the brewery having already been through a complex process. The endosperm of the harvested grain is the store of starch laid down to nourish the early stages of the germination of the seedling.

The conversion from the insoluble carbohydrate to soluble sugars is by the action of the enzymes in the grain. In the industrial process of malting the barley grain is sprayed with warm water and kept at a temperature of 15–20 °C for three days. Germination occurs and is later stopped by raising the temperature. The enzyme action ceases and the germinated grains are dried in kilns and after a period 24–48 hours of roasting at temperatures of 70–100°C are crushed between rollers. The malted barley is now known as **grist**.

Small breweries buy the cultures of yeast but the biggest ones have their own microbiological laboratories and work to develop new strains.

Recipe

Take 2–2.5 barrels of 'liquor', a couple of pints of sulphuric acid, and some gypsum.
Add a quarter of malted grains.
Boil with the dried female flowers of *Humulus lupulus* (hops – a member of the Cannabinaceae family).
Add 0.1 ppm zinc and 2 pounds of yeast per barrel.

Not exactly modern SI units – but the small brewery works to a very old recipe to produce traditional ales. (A barrel is a measure of 36 gallons or 165 litres. A quarter is three hundredweight = 336 lb = 150 kg. 'Liquor' is the brewery term for water.)

(a) A mixture of different malted grains is used. Malted winter barleys with varieties known as chocolate, amber, pale ale and crystal, depending on the length of the roasting period, impart different characteristics. It is important that varieties used have a low nitrogen content (otherwise a haze develops in the finished product). A small proportion of malted wheat is used to help 'head retention'. New varieties of grain arrive on the market regularly – the work of the plant breeder is combined with the skill of the maltster to produce a better malted grain for the industry.

(b) The grist is crushed between rollers in the grist mill, mixed with 'liquor' (hot water) in a mash tun and the enzymes are reactivated so that a 'sweet wort' – a sugary solution – can be washed out. The waste of the barley is converted to animal food. The water supply to the brewery must be treated to give it the prized qualities of the natural water at Burton-on-Trent. Sulphuric acid is added to get rid of the natural carbonates, then gypsum (calcium sulphate) and calcium chloride are added.

(c) The sweet wort is transferred to the copper kettles and boiled with hops to pick up the bitter flavour. (Picture shows hops being added to the boiling wort.) The spent hops are sold as hop manure.

(d) Hop plants and oast houses where the hops are dried. Some hops are imported but there are hop fields in Kent and the Midlands.

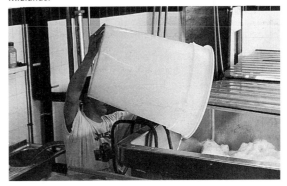

(e) Yeast is 'pitched' into the tanks of cooled hopped wort (to each 360 litres of wort is added 2 kg yeast slurry saved from the previous fermentation). The lag phase of yeast growth is shortened by pumping in oxygen to encourage aerobic respiration and rapid growth. The temperature in the vats increases but is kept below 20 °C by pumping chilled water through stainless steel cooling pipes. The temperature controlled fermentation continues for up to six days for ales (at 12–18 °C). In the open vats the froth of CO_2 keeps the fermentation anaerobic. Excess yeast is sold as a health food and in some cases the carbon dioxide is even sold to gasify soft drinks.

(f) After settling and filtration the beer is cleared with 'finings' (alginates and isinglass). The final stages of maturing (conditioning) to develop distinctive flavours occur in wooden casks, metal kegs or in the bottles. Some beers are filtered and sold in this live state but most are pasteurised (flash heated) to prevent spoilage.

A flow diagram of the brewing of beer can be seen in the question on page 55.

The small scale process may seem a little haphazard but it is controlled by qualified scientists and carried out under sterile conditions. The spoilage of one fermentation of 400 litres would be a considerable loss. Microbiological tests are done at all stages to ensure hygiene and samples halfway through and at the end of each batch are plated out on different agars which would detect the presence of wild yeasts or spoilage microbes.

■ FERMENTATION

The ancient art of brewing, one of the oldest of the biotechnologies, has provided countless people over the years with pleasure, an occupation and/or an income. It is difficult to date the earliest brewing industries. Egyptologists point to the pyramid hieroglyphs as early illustrations of the process and historians are certain that beer was being brewed in ancient Babylon (now Iraq) about 8000 years ago. (See *Biology Advanced Studies - Human and Social Biology*.) It is likely that on many occasions and in many areas the 'accidental spoiling' of fermenting fruit juice would have provided an attractive beverage for even earlier biotechnologists.

The term 'fermentation' was originally used for processes such as the brewing of wine, beer and also to some extent for the manufacture of cheese, butter and yogurt. It was thought of as the metabolism of microbes in a liquid medium and in the absence of oxygen – in other words, as the anaerobic metabolism of a carbon-source substrate to make a useful product. The definition has now been extended, in common use, to include all processes in which microbes can be made to manufacture something that we need. (See Chapter 4 for a more precise definition of fermentation.)

Traditionally the fermentation processes of food production relied on the microbes present in the environment; for wines, on the surface of the grapes; for cheeses, in the dairies and store rooms; and for sauerkraut, on the cabbage leaves. In modern manufacture the microbes are cultured under sterile laboratory conditions and little is left to chance.

(It is estimated that in 1979 the world production of beer was eight million tonnes – about 136 000 000 000 pints. In the same year fermentation worldwide also produced 1 750 000 tonnes of baker's yeast – see below.)

■ Fermentation on a solid substrate

Fungi obtain their nutrients and energy by breaking down organic material – they are **chemoheterotrophs**. The yeasts in the brewing examples use sugars from fruit juice or digested starch. In baking, the yeast also uses the flour as a substrate but in this case the substrate is a semi-solid dough.

■ Baker's yeast and fermentation of a solid substrate

Baking in Britain until about 1780 was always by the 'sour dough' method – using just flour and water and the natural yeasts. The dough soured

Product	Manufacturing country	Energy source/substrate	Microbe
Alcoholic drinks			
Beer	Most	Barley	*Saccharomyces cerevisiae*
Booza	Egypt	Wheat	Mixed microbes
Chicha	S America	Maize	Mixed moulds and bacteria
Pulque	Mexico	Agave	*S. cerevisiae* and others
Sake	Japan	Rice	*S. sake* and *Aspergillus*
Tej	Ethiopia	Honey	*Saccharomyces oryzae*
Foods			
Cheddar cheese	UK	Milk	*Streptococcus lactis*, *Lactobacillus casei*
Laban rayeb (curd cheese)	Egypt	Milk	*S. lactis*, *S. kefir* and coliform bacteria
Yogurt	Many	Milk	*L. bulgaricus* and *S. thermophilus*
Tempe	Indonesia	Soya bean	*Rhizopus sp.*
Shoyu (soy sauce)	China, Korea, Japan	Wheat and soya	*Aspergillus sp.* etc.
Sauerkraut	Germany	Cabbage	*Lactobacillus sp.*

Table 6.1 Some examples of fermented foods and drinks – various yeasts, moulds and bacteria are used and the product is usually in a form which is suitable for storing a food which would otherwise be spoiled by microbes

for about a week and was then baked. However, a small amount was always saved to continue the next batch.

Today a fresh culture of Baker's yeast is usually used for each batch and and can be obtained either as a compressed cake of the live yeast cells or as dried granules. It could be a by-product of brewing but it is generally produced in a different process and from special strains of bread yeast. A huge yield of yeast results from the aerobic fermentation which uses a low sugar concentration and a high amount of oxygen. The fermentation vessels are stirred by air being blown through the liquid. So although the bread yeast works in dough as a solid substrate fermentation, it is manufactured in a very liquid fermentation medium.

Trays of dough proving

The living yeast metabolises and multiplies rapidly in a warm place, using the sugars in the dough as a **substrate**. ('Substrate' is the general term for the substance on which an enzyme acts.) In this case the enzymes are either present from the original grain or in some bakeries fungal amylase is added. The products of the fermentation, alcohol and carbon dioxide, collect as the dough rises in a warm place and then the bubbles expand and the waste products (alcohol, carbon dioxide and water) are driven off as the bread is baked.

Some biotechnologists are working on gene transfer (see page 79) to introduce changes in the gluten and enzymes of the wheat to improve industrial bread making.

Garden compost heap

A garden compost heap is another good example of a solid state fermentation. Under the right conditions the dead vegetable matter is broken down by saprobiotic microbes. They use the products for growth and reproduction and also for metabolism, during which heat is generated and the compost heap warms up. Soil microbes are essential in removing dead organic material for recycling and maintaining the fertility of the soil. Wild mushrooms (see the organism file on page 18) are saprobionts (i.e. they are chemoheterotrophs living on dead or decaying organic material) growing in fields or woodland and are collected as culinary delicacies. However, the huge demand can now only be satisfied by an industrial scale production.

Collecting wild mushrooms

Recipe

Take 400 bales of wheat straw.
Mix with chicken manure from broiler farm.
Hose down with water (which is then recycled).
Continue this for four days, and then allow to stand in yard for nine days (with regular turning to encourage aerobic as well as anaerobic respiration of the microbes). The temperature of the pile has now risen to 50–70 °C.
Compress into 2 m × 2 m stacks 100 m long, mixing with more chicken manure and cotton seed meal (for extra nitrogen) and gypsum (to flocculate the colloids). Leave for six more days of fermentation and then store for heat pasteurisation.

2 m × 2 m stacks of straw in the yard of a mushroom farm

This is the composted straw for mushroom growing. It is wet and has a strong smell of ammonia. The pasteurising at 58 °C kills pests and disease organisms and also reduces the gaseous ammonia from 800 ppm to zero. This is essential because even 5 ppm are toxic to the mushroom spawn. The cooled straw compost is now mixed with mushroom spawn grown on rye grains.

Amount of spawn used / litres of spawn per tonne compost	2.5	5.0	7.5	10.0
Yield of mushrooms / kg per tonne compost	163	179	180	179

Table 6.2 Relationship of mushroom yield to amount of spawn sown

The usual rate of addition is 5 litres per tonne. The spawned compost is packed on shelves to a depth of 15 cm and after 14 days of growth is covered with a white mycelium. The growing tunnels (50 m long) are kept at a humidity of 90–95% and a temperature of 24 °C. As the fermentation continues, carbon dioxide builds up to about 25 000 ppm. This is because there is no fresh air – all air is recycled. When the vegetative growth of the mycelium is complete, the fungus is 'shocked' to change it to the reproductive phase of making mushrooms. Fresh air is introduced to lower the CO_2 content to atmospheric levels and the temperature is dropped. At the same time the mycelium is covered with a layer or casing of soil and peat 7 cm thick. The mycelium has to grow up through this and the pinhead mushrooms start to form on the surface. The casing must be kept wet as the mushrooms grow. (Mushrooms are 95% water, so for every kilogram of mushrooms 18–22 litres of water must be sprayed onto the casing.) 17 days after casing, the first flush (about 2.5 lb per square foot) of mushrooms is ready for cutting. After more watering, a similar crop can be cut on day 27. The final flush of about 1 lb per square foot is cut after three more days of watering. The whole growing tunnel is cleaned out and steam sterilised at 70 °C for 12 hours before the next crop.

Q What is the SI equivalent of 2.5 lb per square foot?

Ready to start cutting the first flush. There is a bank, six shelves high, on each side of the central gangway. The tunnel is one of eighty, each 50 m long, at one of the biggest mushroom growers in the UK.

■ Liquid fermentation – wine making

This technique obviously differs from solid substrate fermentation because the microbes are growing in a liquid medium. The home winemaker pours the boiled grape (or other fruit) juice and a culture of yeast into a sterile jar. The pH is adjusted and some nutrients added. Then, apart from keeping it all at an optimum temperature and allowing gases to escape through a gas trap, there is little that needs to be done until harvest. The system is a very simple version of the laboratory fermenter (Fig. 5.4) and during the period of fermentation the yeast will have grown using the sugars in the fruit juice. A typical growth curve over time for a bacterial culture is shown in Fig. 5.13. The curve for yeast biomass increase in liquid culture in a sugar medium is similar. In a laboratory fermenter it is possible to monitor throughout the indicators of growth, i.e. the number of yeast cells, amount of alcohol, production of carbon dioxide (and hence change in pH) and the decrease in the amount of sugar in the medium. Such changes are indicated in the graph (Fig. 6.1).

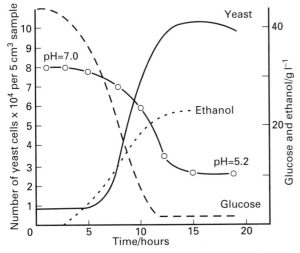

Figure 6.1 Graph showing some of the indicators of growth and fermentation in a closed batch culture

Answer the following question using Fig. 6.1.

Q (a) Estimate from the graph the number of yeast cells per cm³ at the start and at the end of the fermentation period.
(b) What is the most likely reason for the ending of the log phase of yeast growth?
(c) What could be done at 15 h to restart yeast growth?
(d) What other changes in the vessel could have caused the start of the stationary phase?

This type of fermentation using a volume of the medium which is not changed is known as **batch fermentation** and is typical of beer brewing and wine-making. (See also Chapter 5.)

For wines, the fermentation process is the same as in a brewery. Yeast metabolises sugars to produce an alcoholic liquid. The difference is that grape juice is used instead of a sweet wort (and no hops are used). About 25 million acres of vineyards are cultivated in the world and the world wine harvest is enough to supply each person with eight bottles per year. About three-quarters of the world's wine is made in Europe, though the percentage made in America, South Africa and Australasia is increasing. France, Spain, Italy and Germany are the traditional vineyards of Europe.

The grape (*Vitis vinifera*) is in nature a climbing plant of the lowland woods in the Mediterranean region. It favours a warm climate with plenty of water and must be treated to prevent pest and disease damage (copper sulphate sprays against mildew). Between 1860 and 1890 all of the French vineyards were destroyed by *Phylloxera* – an insect whose larvae kill the roots of the vine. At present all European vines are grafted on to resistant rootstocks. Grape varieties are selected for suitability for the area, flavour, sugar concentration, colour and disease resistance. The grower picks the grapes when they are mature, the sugar level has risen and the acidity is low but before the rains and frosts. The vintage is different in each area but in central France it usually starts in late September and unless mechanical harvesters are used takes about two weeks. Then the juices are fermented (with or without skins to give red or white wines respectively) using the natural yeasts found on the grapes. In some countries wines are made in sterile factories with a cultured yeast. The quality of the wine from these producers is always consistent.

English vineyard in Surrey

Measurement of sugar-content of grape – specific gravity	1.060	1.080	1.100	1.110	1.125
% potential alcohol vol/vol	7.5	10.0	12.5	13.8	15.6

Table 6.3 How the final amount of alcohol in a wine can be related to the original specific gravity of the grape juice. (This depends on the sugar concentration.)

Complete fermentation of all of the sugar produces a dry wine with a maximum alcohol concentration of just over 15% as the yeast is unable to survive in a higher concentration of its own waste product – alcohol.

Traditional winemaking in France

Taking a sample of fermenting wine to check specific gravity, California

■ Pharmaceutical fermentations

The baking, brewing and dairy products industries can be thought of as developments from an 'ancient biotechnology'. The 'second age of biotechnology' started with the work of Alexander Fleming and the application of techniques to produce antibiotics.

Penicillium is a genus of the aerobic fungi that can be grown on agar plates. The one that was first cultured after Fleming found it contaminating a culture plate and inhibiting the growth of bacteria was *Penicillium notatum*, although *P. chrysogenum* was soon found to be an even more effective species. The industry now uses many different strains and a host of other antibiotic producing organisms, as well as some semi-synthetic forms (see page 54).

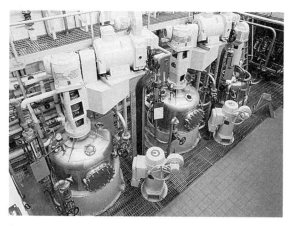

Commercial fermentation units for the production of biological products, such as interferon, using genetically engineered cultures of bacteria, viruses or microorganisms

Alexander Fleming (1881-1955)

Alexander Fleming in his laboratory at St Mary's Hospital in 1909

Working at St Mary's Hospital, London, he first observed the famous Petri dish in 1928. He realised that the fungus was producing a chemical that diffused through the agar. It was either slowing down or preventing bacterial growth. He set about extracting the chemical and produced the first crude samples of what he named Penicillin. He then supervised clinical tests with patients to see if his 'antibiotic' would also inhibit the growth of microbe pathogens *in vivo*. The technology advanced slowly and in wartime Britain the cultures were being grown in the only available glassware, hospital bedpans. The production research was transferred to the USA where the development was rapid and by the latter stages of the war enough penicillin was being produced to treat the British and American casualties.

Fleming was honoured in his lifetime for this discovery, the developments of which have saved countless lives, and he will be remembered as the 'father of antibiotic therapy'. When asked about his 'accidental discovery' he quietly replied by quoting Louis Pasteur – 'all scientists should treasure the exceptions'.

A page from his notebook

You should note that all antibiotic production is **secondary metabolism** – i.e. at a special period in the life of the organism when there is a change away from its optimum conditions. The **primary metabolism** is the norm, when the organism is breaking down a substrate to release energy and producing an increase in its own biomass; at this time little antibiotic would be produced. (See Chapter 4.)

From growing the microbes on agar in a Petri dish to fermenting thousands of litres in a full scale industrial plant requires much research, complex engineering and techniques of scaling-up through laboratory fermenters and pilot plants. (See Fig. 5.4 and the photographs on page 52 and the cover.) Some of the problems of this process are illustrated by the Pruteen example on pages 56-7.

SCIENTIST FILE

**Martin Cole, PhD, DSc, CBiol, FIBiol –
Director of Research, SmithKline Beecham,
Brockham Park**

*How I became interested in substances made by
microorganisms*

When studying biology at Imperial College, London,
I was fascinated by microorganisms because of
their sinister side in causing diseases, as well as
their diverse forms and biochemical activities. In
my PhD studies I looked at the process by which
they invaded plant tissues.

Why was it that some microbes invaded healthy
tissues easily and others only poorly or not at all?
So I was introduced to microbiological research
and the vast array of enzymes and other chemicals
made by microbes and plants. I found that naturally
occurring inhibitors were controlling enzyme
activity and had my first publication in the journal
Nature. I also found how easy it was to get dis-
tracted from the main object of a research project
when I found a new species of *Pseudomonas*
growing in the acidic environment of apple tissue!

A major change in my life occurred as a result
of responding to an advertisement in the *Daily
Telegraph*. I was interviewed and appointed to the
Beecham Research Laboratories where I worked
on the penicillin nucleus, 6-amino penicillanic acid
(6APA). The laboratories were the converted
maids' bedrooms on the top floor of an old house.
Later, new specially designed labs were built in
the grounds.

The research led to improved ways of making
6APA by using microbial enzymes to remove
the side chain from the penicillin molecule. Then
by acylation of the amino group of 6APA the new
'semi-synthetic' penicillins were produced and
assessed. A big team effort led to the development of compounds such as cloxacillin for
treating penicillin resistant staphylococcal
infections and amoxycillin, a broad spectrum oral
penicillin for a wide range of infections. Sales of
these new penicillins made Beecham grow into
an international pharmaceutical company.

My earlier interest in enzyme inhibition was
rekindled by the work on β-lactamases. These
compounds are bacterial enzymes that can
confer resistance to penicillins. It took many
years of effort before an inhibitor that could
be taken by mouth was found. It had to block
the action of enough types of β-lactamase to
render a wide range of resistant bacteria sensitive to amoxycillin. We checked synthetic
compounds and microbial metabolites but success only came when we were looking at a soil
organism *Streptomyces clavuligerus* which
was shown to produce substances known as
cephalosporins.

We found that *S. clavuligerus* makes a potent β-lactamase inhibitory substance which
was isolated and named clavulanic acid. It was
a completely new type of compound and there
was great excitement in the lab. After much
further work on its properties it was taken
orally by volunteers. Fortunately, it reached the
bloodstream in a sufficient concentration to be
clinically active, and was then released in the
urine. A new drug, Augmentin (clavulanic acid,
as its K salt, co-formulated with amoxycillin)
was marketed by Beecham (now SmithKline
Beecham) and patented around the world (the
inventors being M. Cole, T.T. Howard and C.
Reading). Worldwide sales in 1993 were reported to have topped US $1 billion.

There is still much scope for exploring the
products of microorganisms and plants. I have
now retired, but research continues in an attempt
to overcome other problems of antibiotic
resistance and to find improved treatments for
infectious diseases.

Brewers make artificial blood discovery
Robin McKie, Science Correspondent

Artificial blood made by yeast and brewed in vats may soon provide life-saving treatments for accident victims. This startling concept could become reality within three years thanks to a genetic-engineering project carried out by Delta Biotechnology – a subsidiary of the brewers, Bass.

Delta's scientists have exploited their parent company's brewing expertise to find a stable form of yeast that can make haemoglobin, the protein that gives blood its red colour and carries oxygen to tissues round the body.

Scientists at Delta Biotechnology have succeeded in inserting the genes for human alpha and beta globin into yeast genes. As a result, the yeast makes the globins and haem in such a way that they combine to produce haemoglobin.

By brewing this yeast, haemoglobin can now be made on a large scale. However, this is not the same as making artificial blood. To do that, researchers will have to get round one other considerable problem – pure haemoglobin is poisonous.

Without the protective protein coat that surrounds a red-blood cell, pure haemoglobin can cause kidney damage and chemical destruction of blood vessels, so an artificial equivalent of the red blood cell coat must be created before 'yeast blood' can be used on humans.

The Observer, 17 February 1991

Q The diagram below shows the sequence of processes involved in the brewing of beer.

(a) Describe the changes occurring in the barley grains in the vessel labelled A.

(b) The malt mill (B) dries and crushes the barley sprouts. State *one* effect this has on the sequence of processes.

(c) The nutrient-rich liquor is called sweet wort. Suggest *one* use for the residues which have been separated from the liquor and removed at C.

(d) Suggest *one* substance the brewer might add to the mash tun in order to get a low-carbohydrate or 'lite' beer.

(e) Suggest *one* reason why the sweet wort is boiled at D.

(f) (i) Identify E which is added to the fermentation tank.

(ii) Describe exactly what is happening in the fermentation tank to produce beer.

(g) (i) Give the economic importance of *one* product removed at F.

(ii) State *one* further process which the beer undergoes at G and explain why this is necessary.

(London, A-Level Biology, 1992.)

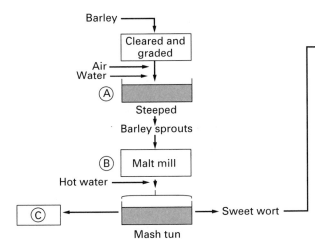

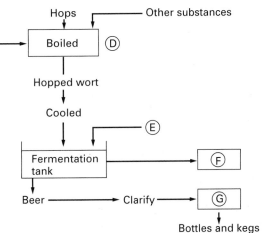

Figure 6.2

CHAPTER 7
BIOTECHNOLOGY - INDUSTRIAL PROCESS

In the previous chapter we considered some processes that have developed from small cottage industries to huge commercial enterprises.

For new processes the costs of research and development are offputting to most industrialists. One example from a food production project will show some of the difficulties. In 1967 the company ICI identified a need for a low cost, large yielding protein production system that would be cheaper than soya bean protein for cattle food. They decided that the best new source would be SCP, single cell protein – in other words, growing microorganisms as a food. In theory, the protein from microbes is just as nutritious as cheese, eggs or fish. But would customers find it acceptable? There were already examples of microbes being used as foods, e.g. yeast products such as Marmite and a protein-rich biscuit made from the blue green (cyano) bacteria *Spirulina platensis* from Chad and Mexico. So ICI set up a research team to search for suitable microbes that would ferment, and grow, on readily available substrates (feedstock) which were a cheap source of carbon and nitrogen. They had available methanol (a carbon source) produced from the methane in North Sea gas and ammonia (a nitrogen source). They found an ideal organism, the flagellate that they named *Methylophilus methylotrophus*. (Greek for methanol liking and eating.) It had lots of advantages.

• It causes no disease.
• It has a high conversion rate from feedstock to protein.
• Cells can be separated from the medium easily.
• The cells have a good nutritional value with a high amino acid content.
• Growth occurs with a low demand for oxygen and minerals.
• There is a rapid rate of growth at 37°C.

The scientists worked on the organism, including some DNA technology, and the engineers worked on scaling up the laboratory fermenters. By 1975 they were ready to manufacture the reactor, a huge 42 metre high tower that was 11 metres in diameter at the top. Production started in 1981. One million litres of sterilised medium were used and 0.4 kg of

Cans of dried *Spirulina* algae – a protein-rich health food

the microbe culture added. Air was blown through at a rate of 80 000 cubic metres an hour, both for the metabolism of the organism and to stir and circulate the medium. After 30 hours of fermentation the biomass of the bacterium in the culture was 30 tonnes. At this stage harvesting started. As some of the SCP rich medium was removed new sterile medium was run in. This continuous harvesting is a good example of **continuous fermentation** (as compared to batch fermentation – Chapters 5 and 6). **Down stream processing** is the term used for the processes applied to the harvested culture. It includes heating to kill the microbes, filtration of the cells from the medium, separation of the protein and drying of the product that they called **Pruteen**. The process was a great *scientific* success – the continuous fermentation production had runs of over 100 days and yielded the excellent output of 6000 tonnes per month. In 1978 they predicted that by 1990 they would be able to increase that to one million tonnes a year of high quality Pruteen cattle food.

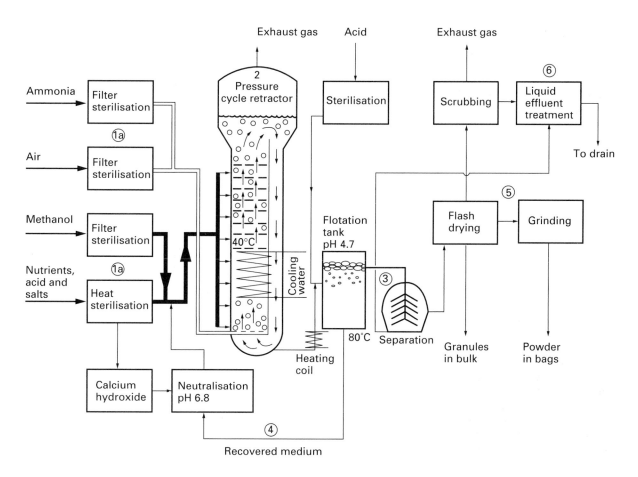

Figure 7.1 The Pruteen process

So what went wrong? The price of soya fell and the cost of North Sea oil increased. Methanol was in demand and became too expensive for a feedstock. So the process could no longer be considered a *commercial* success. After a capital expenditure of £45 million the Pruteen process was closed down. The giant fermenter was used for other products, but has now been dismantled.

The Pruteen story shows that developments in biotechnology are exciting but constrained by technological, social and economic factors, as well as biological aspects.

One SCP product that has been very successful commercially is the fungal SCP sold as **Quorn**™. The fungus *Fusarium graminearum*, which was originally isolated from soil on a football pitch, is grown on a substrate of grain and flour wastes (left over from a low starch bread) and harvested as a

Pack of Quorn

mycelium. It has many advantages. It can be compressed into sheets and the fibres can be made to take on the form of beef or chicken chunks. It is rich in protein and fibre, low in salt and cholesterol and tasteless – so can be given almost any flavour before or during cooking. It was an ideal novel food. It is interesting that the producers refer to it, in promotion material and on packets, not as a fungus or a mould but as being 'mushroom-like' and a 'mycoprotein'. Public acceptability is a very important factor in the commercial success of the products of biotechnology.

A technician wears clean-room clothing to make adjustments to a fermenter unit used for the biotechnological production of cloned protein

■ ENZYME PRODUCTION

You will already know some of the uses of enzymes from microorganisms (see page 44). One of the earliest applications of microbially produced enzymes was probably the removal of blood protein stains from butchers' clothing – this first biological washing powder was produced in 1913. A more recent textile use is of a mixture of cellulase and amylase for whitening and softening 'stone-washed' jeans.

Industrial enzyme use	Market value/ US $ million
Pharmaceutical proteins	100.0
Detergents	70.0
Dairy industry (e.g. rennin)	50.0
Research and development	42.0
Starch products	31.0
Diagnostic enzymes	16.0
Textiles	12.0
Drinks	11.0
Baking	4.5
Biotransformations	4.5
Other uses (estimate)	59.0
Total for year	$400.0

Table 7.1 The estimated market value of the industrial use of enzymes in 1990

Enzymes are biological catalysts. They are proteins made in cells according to the DNA/RNA code and they act to bring about the conversion of one chemical to another. Enzyme technology has become one of the most important features of modern biotechnology as can be seen from Table 7.1. The reason is, of course, that if the right enzyme can be extracted, it can be used to bring about the same type of complex and specific reaction in an industrial process that it catalyses in the cell's metabolism. The enzymes can be extracted from an organism that already produces it in large amounts (e.g. rennin for cheesemaking was taken from young milk-fed calves). In addition, the new techniques of molecular biology can be used to remove the nucleic acid for the enzyme gene from one organism, transfer it into a suitable microbe, and then grow that microbe either in batch or continuous culture. For example, the rennin gene is now transferred into microbes and a safe, pure supply of the enzyme is produced as a secondary metabolite in fermenters – hence the availability of so-called 'vegetarian cheese'.

■ Cheesemaking

Traditional cheesemaking depended on the natural microorganisms present in the dairy and in the milk. Microbes sour the milk, producing lactic acid and lowering the pH, so that when rennet (from the stomach of young mammals) was added, the milk curdled and separated into solid curds and liquid whey (which was used as a substitute for the full milk food for the calves). The curd was packed into moulds and matured in cool rooms or

58

caves where sometimes local fungi grew on, and through, the cheese to make a 'blue cheese'.

Some delicious cheeses are still made in small amounts by farmers using the old skills, although most of the cheese manufactured today comes from 'factory dairies' using pasteurised milk, really sterile conditions and cultures of lactic acid bacteria and genetically engineered microbial rennet. (This is the common name for the enzyme rennin or renninase.) The manufacture of cheddar-type cheese uses the bacteria *Lactobacillus sp* and *Streptococcus sp* (the abbreviation 'sp' is generally used by biologists to indicate 'one species of the genus'). They cause the change: lactose sugar → lactic acid. The pH change curdles the milk and the rennet causes the formation of the solid curds, a rich mixture of protein and fat. The process of 'cheddaring' cuts the curd into blocks so allowing the whey to drain out. Salt is added and the curd is compressed either in traditional round 'wheels' or in the more usual blocks. Flavour develops over a period of time; the more mature the cheese is, the stronger the flavour. Bacteria and fungi continue the ripening process by metabolising the protein and fat and releasing 'flavour by-products'. Some hard cheeses (like cheddar) mature for 6–9 months, although they can be eaten as mild cheese in a few weeks.

A selection of cheeses

The soft cheeses, such as Camembert and Brie, ripen quickly and are more moist because yeasts grow on the outer surface and form a rind. The blue cheeses such as Stilton and Roquefort have an added fungus, *Penicillium roqueforti*, and are prodded with needles to allow entry of oxygen to the centre of the cheese as the fungus is aerobic. And what about the 'holes' in the Swiss cheese Emmental? The formation of holes is due to another bacterium, *Proprionibacterium shermanii*, that makes proprionic acid (which adds to the flavour) and bubbles of carbon dioxide.

■ Other examples of dairy biotechnology
A form of fermented milk has been produced in most countries where fresh milk is drunk. Yogurt, originating in the Balkans, depends on two bacteria, *Streptococcus thermophilus* to bring the pH of the milk down to 5.5 and *Lactobacillus bulgaricus* to convert the lactose to lactic acid. Incubation takes 12 hours at 32 °C to reach the set state of natural yogurt. The popularity of the product is increased by the addition of sugar and fruit to disguise the acidity. Since the 1960s yogurt production in Britain has greatly increased. Yogurt *is* a nutritious dessert and its manufacture is also an ideal means of using up Europe's excess milk production; it has been well promoted over the last 30 years. An interesting milk product, kefir, seems to have been made in Scandinavia, Georgia and Russia for thousands of years. *Lactobacilli*, *Streptococci* and other bacteria and yeasts in milk grow on and penetrate grains of milk solids. The grains are washed and added to milk in a bag. In a warm place the microbes grow in clusters and are described as kefir grains. After 24 hours the milk is strained

Modern cheesemaking – 'cheddaring'

and the fizzy, slightly alcoholic beverage consumed. The kefir grains are washed and added to fresh milk to start another brew. One newspaper report rather enthusiastically hyped kefir as 'the elixir of long life' because some Georgian peasants had been reported to live for 120 years.

Butter is made from pasteurised cream which is chilled and churned to beat it into an emulsion of water-in-oil to which salt is added as a preservative. However, before the churning it may have been incubated for 12 hours at 10 °C with *Streptococcus cremoris* and other bacteria to develop flavour.

Soy sauce

Monosodium glutamate or MSG is frequently seen in the ingredients lists of foods. It is a seasoning or 'flavour enhancer' and used to be produced from soya bean protein. However, with huge sales worldwide it is now produced by bacteria which have been selected because of their high yield of L–glutamic acid.

■ Vinegar manufacture

Recipe

Fill an old barrel with oak wood shavings.
Drill a number of holes in the side for aeration.
Pour a few pints of stale beer or cider over the shavings.
Allow cider or malt wort to trickle through.

Churning butter in a creamery

■ Soya bean biotechnology

The Chinese and Koreans developed the methods of making a sauce called shoyu and are reputed to have exported it to Japan over 1000 years ago. Cooked soya beans were exposed to natural microbes such as the fungi *Aspergillus sp* and *Rhizopus sp* which fermented the beans for several months. The early 'biotechnologists' then boiled the mouldy beans with salty water and allowed the resulting liquid to ferment further. The modern Japanese method works to much tighter specifications and cultures of *Aspergillus oryzae* are inoculated into a sterile wheat and soya bean mix and kept in fermentation tanks before filtration and pasteurisation.

The wheat and soya bean waste of this process is converted into a protein rich food, miso paste. The Indonesian foods tempe kedele and kecap are made by fermenting soya beans with *Rhizopus sp.*

Stale cider or malt wort trickles in

Wood shavings covered with growth of vinegar bacteria

Vinegar (ethanoic acid) collects

Figure 7.2 The old vinegar barrel method of making vinegar

The aerobic *Acetobacter* grows over the wood shavings for a few days and converts the alcoholic brew to vinegar:
ethanol → ethanoic acid.
$CH_3.CH_2.OH \rightarrow CH_3.COOH$

Wine vinegar is made when the substrate is the ethanol in wine and the fermentation is usually done in large open vats. Since ethanoic (acetic) acid is widely used commercially other, more efficient, less traditional methods of manufacture are essential. Microbial breakdown of cellulose to ethanoic acid is a promising project as there is so much plant cellulose readily available.

■ Returning to enzymes

Each process already described has been brought about not just by the microbe but, more specifically by the enzymes that are part of its metabolism. When whole microbes are used, as in yeast fermentations and cheese manufacture, the microbes use up some of the substrate for their own primary metabolism. In some processes this is a disadvantage and there is also the problem that the cells need to be removed from the product. It is often easier to use the microbe in fermenting a substrate to produce the extracellular enzyme. The whole culture medium can then be treated by down stream processing techniques and the enzyme can be separated and purified. In the main industrial processes the purified enzyme can be used in an efficient and cost effective way. For example, it would not be convenient to soak clothes in microbe cultures in order to remove stains. Bacterial extracellular enzymes are made and added to biological washing powders. The lipases digest fats, amylases break down starch and proteases catalyse the breakdown of proteins. The end products of these reactions are all soluble and can be washed out from the cloth. Each enzyme is a protein and has an optimum temperature for its activity – some have been selected to operate at temperatures as high as 70 °C. The annual world production of proteases is over 500 tonnes and this is about 40% of the total amount of all enzymes manufactured. (Only 1 gram is needed for 5 kilograms of washing powder.) Some people are allergic even to low concentrations of these enzymes, so during the preparation of washing powder the enzymes are encapsulated in a soluble membrane.

One much used enzyme is glucose isomerase. It converts glucose to fructose and today fructose syrups are widely used in processed foods, such as soft drinks, cakes, biscuits, sweets, sauces and soups.

Starch → Glucose → Fructose

Q Check how many lists of ingredients on packets include 'sugar' without saying which sort.

The reason why fructose is used is that it is much sweeter than glucose and so is cheaper to use because less is needed. It also sweetens without having a high joulerific value. Cheap starch from corn and other grains can be converted by microbial amylase to the feedstock which is then changed to fructose by glucose isomerase. As the USA increased its use of high fructose corn syrup (HFCS) in the 1980s it reduced its imports of sugar from 6 to 1.5 million tonnes. This was a success for biotechnology but a disaster for the cane sugar growers of countries like the Phillipines where 500 000 workers lost their jobs.

Some enzymes now used in industrial and pharmaceutical processes are very expensive, e.g. 1 mg glucokinase costs £100, but are only needed in minute quantities. Remember that enzymes, like chemical catalysts, are not used up in the processes that they catalyse. Instead of pouring the enzyme in solution into the reaction vessel, it can first be **immobilised** in a matrix such as silica gel, or in alginate beads or within microspheres or semipermeable membranes. The immobilised enzyme is just as effective as the free one and instead of being discarded with the spent medium it can be recovered, filtered off, washed and re-used in subsequent conversions. The technique is very effective in continuous fermentations. A similar process is the use of immobilised whole cells.

■ Food poisoning and food spoilage

Many holidaymakers and travellers return from a visit to a foreign country with lurid tales of trips ruined by several days illness due to food poisoning. Some of these events are due to eating unusual foods, some because of excesses of food, alcohol or sun and others because of pathogenic bacteria. If you bear in mind the fact that under optimum conditions some species of bacteria grow so fast that they can double in numbers every 20 minutes, you will not be surprised to learn that each single bacterial cell contaminating food could produce well over a million descendants in under seven hours. (See page 41.)

If the food is in a warm place then the conditions for growth are optimum – warm, moist and a rich substrate. If the food is already contaminated or handled in an unhygienic manner the potential growth of pathogenic organisms is enormous. We have become increasingly aware in recent years of the contamination of eggs and poultry by *Salmonella enteritidis* (see the organism file on page 90). Undercooked frozen chicken (when the juices

(a) Micro-encapsulation, e.g. in nylon capsules

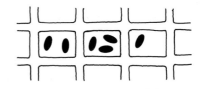

(b) Lattice entrapment, e.g. in alginate or polystyrene

(c) Adsorption on solid surfaces, e.g. alumina, clay and glass

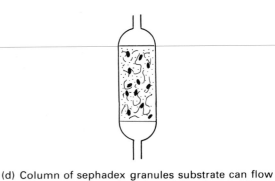

(d) Column of sephadex granules substrate can flow either up or down (e.g. immobilised penicillin acylase for semi-synthetic antibiotics)

Figure 7.3 Methods of immobilising enzymes (or whole cells)

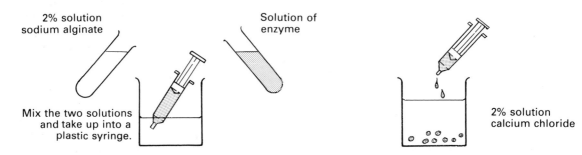

The beads harden in 5 minutes and are washed with distilled water. They are packed in a column and the substrate solution trickles through. Instead of an enzyme solution, a suspension of yeast could be used. A sugar solution would then be used as the substrate.

Figure 7.4 A laboratory method for immobilising enzymes

still run pink), hot or cold, contain the live microbes which can result in the symptoms of vomiting and diarrhoea within 12–36 hours of ingestion. Well over 90% of all cases of food poisoning (salmonellosis) are caused by eating poorly-cooked frozen chickens. The intensive poultry rearing methods now used mean that the pathogen is so common that we should regard all poultry as a potential carrier of disease and cook it well. *Salmonella* causes gastroenteritis because it damages the cells of the intestine epithelium. It is particularly dangerous for old people and babies.

Salmonella typhi causes very serious infection (see the organism file on page 101). It may be found in contaminated drinking water and, where it is often overlooked, in the water used to prepare food or even to wash salads and fruit. It causes typhoid fever which lasts longer than salmonellosis and can be fatal.

Listeria monocytogenes is found in milk and dairy products, particularly those such as soft cheeses that are stored for some time at low temperatures. It has also been associated with prepared coleslaw, chilled salads and pâté. Again the symptoms are more serious for at-risk people, the young, the elderly and pregnant women.

Clostridium botulinum (related to *C. tetani* – see the organism file on page 92) releases one of the most powerful toxins known. It is found in some canned foods and can cause paralysis (botulism) and death.

Aspergillus flavus is a fungus that grows on stored grains and nuts that have been damaged by insects or by rough handling. There have been cases of human deaths (from eating mouldy maize or peanuts for example) and cases of fish and poultry mortality (from food pellets made with mouldy peanuts). The mould grows and the secondary metabolite, a toxin known as aflatoxin, accumulates in the grain or nut. It can cause hepatitis but is also known to be a carcinogen.

The ways to avoid food poisoning at home are obvious. We need to be very careful when preparing our own food or food for others. Perhaps more people should take care when they are eating unfamiliar foods in countries new to them, and avoid food that may have been standing a while in a warm place. If we suspect the standard of hygiene, we should eat elsewhere. We also need to consider that some of the problems that are encountered are due to the increased demand for a variety of low-priced foods.

Q List some of the methods that should be used to prevent microbial contamination of foods, both at home and in catering establishments such as schools, hospitals and restaurants.

Food spoilage can happen when fungi such as *A. flavus* grow on food and make it unusable or when bacteria break down meat to a rotting condition. We see familiar examples at home when we store some foods too long – cheese and oranges may support the bluegreen mycelium of *Penicillium*, bread may develop a white or greyish mould of *Mucor* (see the organism file on page 16) or *Rhizopus*, and potatoes may go soggy due to the enzymes of the soft-rot bacterium *Erwinia*. Fruits like strawberries have a short shelf-life in the shop before being spoiled by microbes. It is interesting to speculate on when technologies developed which enabled people to store foods free from damage by spoilage organisms.

Q When did people learn that some foods could be preserved in saltwater, or that meats coated with salt did not rot?

Q Suggest when and under what conditions the following techniques developed.
(a) Drying and storing vegetables through the winter.
(b) Cutting meat and fish into thin strips and air drying them.
(c) Baking bread so hard that the biscuits lasted for long sea voyages.

Meat and fish have long been preserved by smoking over a wood fire. Some vegetables have been pickled in vinegar and some fruits in alcohol. Other fruits were boiled with sugar to make jams. In all of these methods something was done (dehydration, high osmolarity with sugar or salt, alcohol) to the foods to make them an unsuitable habitat for the spoilage organism. Later technologies worked by sealing meat, fish, fruit and vegetables into jars or cans and heating to a suitable temperature to kill the microbes and most of the resistant spores. Then, following the development of deep refrigeration and the widespread use of home freezers, almost any type of food could be preserved and exported around the world. With modern transport systems it can be the strawberry season every day of the year.

Pasteur's name was given to the method of making milk fairly safe for a few days (heating rapidly to 72 °C, holding for 15 seconds and cooling rapidly) – this method does not kill all organisms, but enough to delay the spoilage process. In order to kill all spoilage organisms another method must be employed – steam sterilisation at temperatures up to 160 °C – this product is known as UHT milk. Some chemicals can be added to foods to preserve them and these usually appear on food labels as E-numbers (e.g. E260, ethanoic acid and E210, benzoic acid). The most recent technology is the use of gamma radiation (often from ^{60}Cobalt). The food does not become radioactive but spoilage organisms and insect pests are killed. There is an active debate on whether the method should be used. It is expensive but is probably the only method that would be effective with certain foods (such as spices and fresh strawberries). There are some doubts about possible chemical damage to the irradiated food. You may think that any food that has been irradiated should be clearly labelled and, as with many other issues in biotechnology, the general public should have enough information to make decisions.

Louis Pasteur (1822-1895)

As a young chemist, Pasteur was the first to discover the properties of isomers. He worked as a chemist in the French wine business and was the first to show that fermentation was not just a chemical change; it was brought about by a living organism, yeast. He also showed that other microorganisms caused the wine to sour and carried out further experiments for the beer brewers.

Some of his writings show that he thought that some microbes produced chemicals that killed other microbes (an early hint at the possibilities of antibiotics). He carried out many experiments on decay and biodeterioration showing that meat broths which went bad when exposed to the air could be preserved when boiled and retained in sealed glass flasks. His famous experiments with swan-necked flasks (which were open to the air but had a U-bend to prevent entry of particles, and microbes, from the air) showed that such sterilised broths could be kept for some time. Some of his broth is still on show at the Pasteur Institute in Paris. Perhaps his most influential medical research followed the chance discovery that weakened microbes do not cause a disease but that the person injected with such weakened microbes develops an immunity. Thus he developed vaccines against cholera, sheep and cattle anthrax and rabies. His name will always be linked with his method of pasteurising wines and milk by short periods of heat treatment.

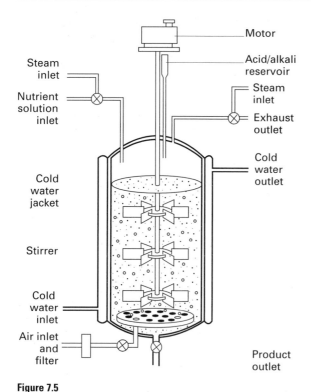

Figure 7.5

Q The diagram shows an industrial fermenter in which microorganisms can be cultured in nutrient solutions to obtain useful products.
(a) Explain why each of the following processes is necessary.
  (i) Aerating the culture
  (ii) Mixing the culture
  (iii) Cooling the culture
(b) How is the fermenter sterilised and why is the process necessary?
(c) How would a continuous culture be maintained in the fermenter?
(d) Name *one* product that could be produced commercially by this method.
(London, A/AS Biology 1990.)

CHAPTER 8

BIOTECHNOLOGY IN AGRICULTURE AND THE ENVIRONMENT

Much of the concern today for the environment is due to the way in which we pollute the sea and waterways. People living in settlements have probably always used rivers and streams as a supply of drinking water and to carry away wastes. The earliest example, in Britain, of a law against pollution seems to be that of 1388 which '... prohibited the throwing of dung, filth and garbage into the ditches, rivers or other waters and places within, about or nigh to any cities, boroughs or towns ...'. In 1535 a law was passed against '... annoying the Thames or casting dung into the river ...'. However, it wasn't until 1848 that a significant Public Health Act was passed. Following the work of Dr John Snow, who investigated the spread of cholera around a street drinking-water pump in London's Soho, the Metropolitan Water Act was passed which prohibited the extraction of Thames water for domestic use. The Thames was, like most urban waterways at that time, an open sewer. The formidable scientist Michael Faraday experienced it at first hand. He carried out experiments, dropping his visiting cards into the river and noting that they disappeared from view when barely one inch below the surface. He wrote to the editor of *The Times* on July 7 1854:

'Sir, I traversed this day by steamboat the space between London and Hungerford Bridge ... it was low water ... the appearance and smell of the river forced themselves upon my attention. The whole river was an opaque pale brown fluid. The smell was very bad ... the whole river was for a time a real sewer. If we neglect this ... (soon) a hot season will give us sad proof of the folly of our carelessness.' Later that year the proof came – a major cholera outbreak, to be followed by another in 1866. By that time people understood that disease was linked with sewage contamination. A couple of decades later Pasteur and Koch were able to demonstrate that water-borne diseases were caused by bacteria.

From that time there was a gradual improvement in Britain in the attitude to public health and standards were established for water supply, sewage disposal and water pollution. In industrialised countries citizens can expect to have a

FARADAY GIVING HIS CARD TO FATHER THAMES;
And we hope the Dirty Fellow will consult the learned Professor.

supply of clean domestic water and a system for the removal of domestic and industrial waste. However in many developing countries these features do not exist and the mortality rates from typhoid, cholera and other water-borne diseases are high. In every day of the year 1980 over 50 000 people worldwide died because of contaminated water. In developing countries there has been some improvement between 1980 and 1988 in water supply. In urban areas the number getting a supply of water increased from 76 to 78% of the population and in rural areas it increased from 31 to 56%. However it was calculated that in 1988 201 million of the 325 million people living in 20 African countries still lacked access to safe drinking water.

■ HAPPY HOLIDAYS?

You will have read (page 61) about food poisoning and are sure to have seen newspaper reports about recent cases. It is little wonder that the main resorts of Europe are unable to maintain hygiene when they have such massive tourist invasions for a couple of months of each year. Over 90% of all municipal sewage discharged into the Mediterranean in 1988 had no treatment at all.

 Consider what the future situation could be, using these statistics.

Year	Number of tourists to Mediterranean region/millions
1986	117
2000	162–409 (est.)
2025	379–758 (est.)

 The scheme below shows how infected humans can pass on pathogens to others. Try to work out at which points the microbiologist could be employed to lessen the dangers.

 Now read the extract from *The Observer* of 24 July 1994 and compare the situation in Hong Kong with that studied by Michael Faraday.

Poisonous tide laps at shores of Hong Kong
Catherine Field, Hong Kong

It is summer in Hong Kong. In the past month, one person has died of cholera symptoms and at least 22 cases have been reported. The outbreak is linked to contaminated seawater used in restaurants to keep prawns, lobsters, crabs and fish alive.

Occasional incidences of cholera are nothing new to Hong Kong, but what has alarmed the public this time is that the water for the restaurants has been drawn from the harbour – one of the most polluted stretches of water in the world – and its bacteria-ridden coastline.

Experts predict the once-beautiful Pearl Delta, with Hong Kong at its heart, will become an environmental catastrophe within a decade, an uninhabitable sprawl befouled in air, soil and water.

'Hong Kong's future is as a financial and communications centre, but I think the environment will become so unpleasant it just won't be accepted as a world class city,' predicts May Ng, the Hong Kong director of Friends of the Earth.

In Hong Kong harbour, the incidence of *E. coli*, a bacterium which dwells in the intestine, is up to 1,000 times accepted world norms. Each day enough sewage is poured out to fill 1,000 Olympic-sized swimming pools – only 10 per cent of the sewage receives primary treatment, 40 per cent is 'broken up', and 50 per cent is pumped out raw. Each day, the territory disgorges enough toxic waste to equal the weight of a double-decker bus.

The Observer, 24 July 1994

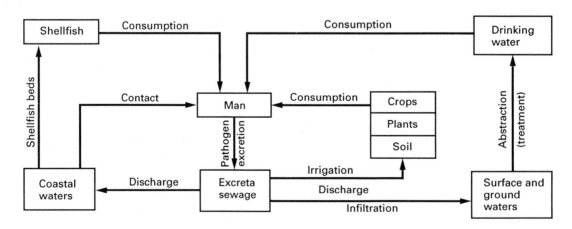

Figure 8.1 The main pathways of human exposure to pathogens in the aquatic environment

Or what about a city holiday? The River Seine carries an increased loading of sewage. The measure of coliforms (*E. coli* of faecal origin) increased from 10 to 500 per cm^3 between 1920 and 1980. The World Health Organisation standard for drinking water is 0 coliforms per 100 cm^3. In Nepal levels of 4800 coliforms are frequently recorded – so take care if you visit Kathmandu!

■ WATER EXTRACTION AND TREATMENT

The water supply system in Bristol is typical of many cities. The people could have a supply of water from local **springs** or from the specially constructed **reservoirs**, from the **river** Severn or a linked **canal** or even from deep **boreholes**. Water from each source requires different treatment. The spring and borehole water is already quite clean, uncontaminated by effluents and with very few living organisms. Reservoir water is quite safe but water flora and fauna must be removed. Water from rivers and shallow wells is potentially dangerous and careful treatment is essential. In all cases regulations demand that chlorine is used to kill microbes and also that microbiological tests are carried out to confirm the cleanliness.

The stages in one scheme of water treatment are illustrated in Fig. 8.3 on page 73.
1. Water, from whatever source, passes through screens to remove vegetation and debris.
2. In the holding reservoir the fine soil particles settle out and microbes break down any organic matter present in the water.
3. The mixing tank is where most of the chemical treatment occurs. Any unusual colour, taste or smell is removed by the addition of powdered activated charcoal. The pH may need to be adjusted by the addition of lime and the hardness may also have to be changed. Powdered alum flocculates (binds) the suspended particles together into larger particles that sink to the bottom of flocculation tanks.
4. The water is then filtered through rapid filter beds of sand.
5. After this chlorine is added to kill any residual microbes and protect the water in its flow along the water mains to the individual outlets. In some areas fluoride is also added to the water to prevent dental decay caused by microorganisms in the human mouth.

Q Find out the origins of your own supply of domestic water. Is your tap water hard or soft? Is fluoride added? (Check with your water supply company.)

■ SEWAGE SYSTEMS

In Rome in the third century BC engineers had constructed over 250 miles of water channels and 30 miles of raised aqueducts to bring a fresh water supply to the city. It has been estimated that 100 million gallons of water reached the city each day – about 100 gallons per person, roughly the same amount as in a large city today. In addition to this, they had constructed brick and stone drains to take away sewage, flushed by water from public baths, and storm water run-off. Some of these third century BC aquifers and drains still exist. The modern water industry owes much to the Roman engineers but a system of **treatment** has been added to the distribution systems. If the modern water supply industry depends on chemical means of treatment in providing a clean water supply relatively free from harmful microbes, then the sewage industry relies to a large extent on microbes to clean-up contaminated water (**biodegradation**).

Consider the 'river' of contaminated fluid arriving at a sewage works of a large urban area. Each dwelling (unless it has its own sewage system) must be connected to the main drain to which it adds the toilet flushings (faeces, urine, paper and chemicals), kitchen wastes (food remains, washing water, detergents and bleach) bath and shower water (with soap and oils) and large volume of dirty water from laundry, house cleaning and car washing. In addition to this, rain water from the streets drains into the sewers from roadside gutters carrying soil, road grit, oil and rubbish. The third major input to the sewers comes from industry. A great deal of water is used, and then goes to waste, in the manufacture of almost everything that you can imagine. From many food factories the waste water has a high organic content. Some discharge water with toxic chemicals. Today, most industries are required by law to clean their water before allowing it to enter public sewers. So, you now have some idea of what reaches the sewage works – 1% solids and 99% water.

It was formerly believed that small amounts of domestic sewage discharged into rivers had a minimal effect as the river 'cleaned itself' over a short distance. (See Fig. 8.2.) An excuse was also given for tipping untreated sewage into the sea – the dilution effect made it harmless! We no longer accept these views. The amount and complexity of contaminated water produced by communities requires effective treatment. We must remember that after treatment this water is often returned to a river from which water is extracted again. It must, therefore, be colourless and odourless; harmful microbes must have been removed and the organic content and toxic chemicals should have been reduced to safe levels.

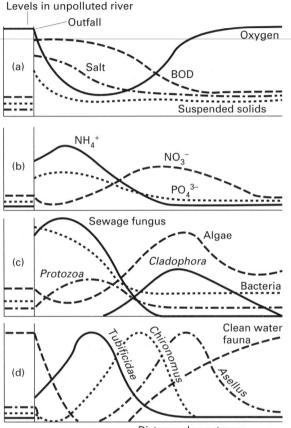

Figure 8.2 The river cleaning itself. The levels measured change dramatically with the input of sewage effluent. However over a distance there is an improvement in chemical and physical properties of the water, resulting in flora and fauna typical of unpolluted rivers.

■ SEWAGE TREATMENT

1. **Primary treatment**. The raw sewage flows through grids that remove large solid debris carried along the sewer pipes. The flow rate is slowed down and the stones and road grit settle (often to be cleaned and reused). In these **sedimentation tanks** some of the organic material will also settle out as a sludge.

Trickling filter bed

Aeration tanks at an activated sludge plant

2. **Secondary treatment**. The liquid effluent from the primary process is treated by a method which accelerates the natural degradation process by aerobic microbes. The older method is the **trickling filter** technique. A revolving pipe allows effluent to trickle through a round bed of stones and clinker. Each surface is coated with a complex community of bacteria, worms, fungi, insect larvae and protozoa. They break down, and feed on, the organic material and the effluent from the bottom of the filter bed may go direct into rivers or it may be held in settling tanks.

The alternative method, where larger amounts of sewage are handled, is the **activated sludge** process. A mixture of microbes is added to the effluent from the primary treatment. They use the sewage organic matter as a food substrate and metabolise rapidly as aerobic conditions are maintained by bubbling air through the tanks (see Fig. 8.3). Specific microbes are used to digest different components of sewage. Some break down proteins and some lipids; carbon dioxide and water are the end products as well as ammonia and hydrogen sulphide. The effluent from this stage is allowed to settle and the sludge is removed. The water may go directly into rivers. The sludge consists largely of the microbes, a proportion of which is reserved to be mixed in with the next batch.

3. **Tertiary treatment**. If the effluent is needed for domestic water supply a further stage of purification is essential. It is similar to the water treatment described earlier.

4. **Sludge treatment**. It has always been a problem to know what to do with the huge amounts of sewage sludge. It has been dried and sold as a fertiliser for farmers and gardeners, it has been buried in landfill sites, dumped at sea and used to generate methane. Perhaps the most effective use is to hold it in insulated tanks where, under anaerobic conditions, microbes produce methane. In some sewage works the methane gas is burned for heating and in others it is used to run a small generator that provides all of the energy needed by the sewage plant.

Q What other methods are used for sewage disposal? Find out the advantages and disadvantages of small 'bio-generators', septic tanks, sewage lagoons and reed-bed systems.

◼ DISCHARGE OF ORGANIC BIOMASS

It is obvious that the ecology of rivers and streams will be greatly changed by the discharge into them of wastes (see *Biology Advanced Studies – Environment and Ecology*). Pollution can be very harmful. It is often unpleasant and we are concerned about dangerous levels of nitrate that can affect health and, together with high levels of phosphate, cause algal blooms and eutrophication. The three most used indicators of water quality are:
* suspended solids, expressed as $mg\ dm^{-3}$
* coliform count, indicates faecal contamination
* biochemical oxygen demand (**BOD**).

BOD is perhaps the most useful. It is a measure of how much oxygen would be removed from water in the breaking down of the organic matter. The most polluted the water the higher the BOD. The water quality classification scheme generally used is shown below.

Using this scheme in 1990 'good quality' was the category for 67% of the rivers in England and Wales, 85% in Northern Ireland and 95% in Scotland.

Description	Class	Current potential use
Good quality	1A BOD <1.5 mg/l	Water of high quality suitable for potable supply abstractions; high class fisheries; high amenity value
	1B BOD <2.0 mg/l	Water of less quality than Class 1A but usable for substantially the same purposes
Fair quality	2 BOD <5.0 mg/l	Waters suitable for potable supply after advanced treatment; supporting reasonably good coarse fisheries; moderate amenity value
Poor quality	3	Waters which are polluted to an extent that fish are absent or only sporadically present; may be used for low grade industrial abstraction purposes; considerable potential for further use if cleaned up
Bad quality	4	Waters which are grossly polluted and are likely to cause nuisance

Table 8.1 River water quality classification scheme (DOE 1986)

Dr Simon Cole - Manager, Microbiological and Chemical Analysis, Wessex Water

Science A-Levels and a fascination for microscopic organisms led me to a microbiology degree course at Bristol University. My third year research project used DNA technology – mapping restriction enzyme sites on bacteriophage DNA. Having achieved a good honours degree I went to do a research degree at York University. I studied the bacteria in the Activated Sludge process (see page 68). I was able to show the limitations of standard culture techniques – more biochemical activity was occurring than could be explained by the apparent number of microorganisms present. Now, we recognise the 'viable but non-culturable' state for many bacteria.

After completing my doctorate I looked for jobs that would combine the microbial genetics of my degree course with the industrial fermentation experience of my research. This was not to be, however, at this stage and I spent three years in my first job as the bacteriologist to a company supplying drinking water to 1.25 million people in the West Midlands.

I have now worked for nine years with Wessex Water who carry out waste water treatment, water supply and river basin management for customers in Dorset, Somerset, Wiltshire and Avon. My job as manager of microbiological and general chemical analysis involves water supply, sewage treatment and diverse aquatic environmental sampling. The main thrust of the laboratory work is the quality assurance of drinking water supplies to meet the stringent standards set down in UK and European law. The techniques we use range from simple routine screening culture tests for 'indicator species' of bacteria to more demanding tests for parasitic protists such as *Cryptosporidium* using microscopy with fluorescent-labelled monoclonal antibodies.

During my time at Wessex Water I have used microbiological tracers, bacterial spores and specific bacteriophages to provide data for modelling water movement in estuaries and marine environments. This has been part of a study assessing the optimum siting and impact of waste water discharges. The laboratory has been working on analysis for emergent pathogens such as *Legionella* and *Cryptosporidium* as well as researching rapid methods of routine screening for indicator bacteria. The use of new test methods and automation would ideally reduce the time taken for quality assurance tests on drinking water from the present 18–24 hours to under six hours. We can already get rapid confirmation of the identity of isolated bacteria such as the faecal indicator species *E. coli* by using gene probes with PCR (the polymerase chain reaction - see page 86). The major area of future development in the industry will be in improving the sensitivity of new DNA techniques to detect specific bacteria to the very low levels (one per 100 cm^3) stipulated by the present drinking water regulations.

■ SOME OTHER ENVIRONMENTAL APPLICATIONS

■ Solid refuse

Those of us who are used to having bins emptied and plastic bags of refuse removed, seldom think about what happens to the resulting rubbish. Some is separated so that glass and metals can be recycled. Most is burned or buried – but landfill sites (holes in the ground) are becoming scarce and, as a result, expensive to use for rubbish. On some tipping sites the methane produced in anaerobic biodegradation is collected and used as a fuel.

■ Reclamation of industrial sites

The 'White Alps' of Cornwall (the china clay spoil heaps) have, to some extent, been recolonised by spraying with a slurry of water, waste paper and fertiliser and the seeds of red and white clover and birdsfoot trefoil. (For further details see *Biology Advanced Studies – Environment and Ecology*.) The plants are nitrogen-fixing leguminous plants and their roots house nodules of bacteria (*Rhizobium trifolii* - see the organism file on page 30) which convert the nitrogen of the air into the nitrates that are needed for plant growth. This enabled the colonising plants to become established and allow other grasses to grow and eventually flourish there. In some places the contaminated areas around old gasworks have been reclaimed. The soil around these ruins is heavily contaminated with cyanides, tars and oils. Yet in this inhospitable habitat some microbes flourish, using the industrial wastes as substrates for their metabolism. The microorganisms were isolated, cultured in the laboratory and sprayed on to the ground to clear up the sites.

■ Oil wastes

Some of the most publicised ecological disasters have been oil spills following shipwrecks, with the consequent death of birds and marine life and pollution of the sea and coast. Some microorganisms are known to metabolise hydrocarbons and will breakdown some of the components of oils. It is possible to use a mixture including *Pseudomonas spp* in clearing small oil spills and also in oil tanks. This is done industrially on a small scale.

■ Metal mining

The spoil heaps of old copper mines frequently contain a small amount of insoluble copper sulphide (less than 0.25%). The bacterium *Thiobacillus oxidans* converts it to soluble copper sulphate which is leached out and can be economically reclaimed. Microbes have also been used to extract from low grade uranium wastes and, experimentally, from other metal ores.

■ BIOTECHNOLOGY IN AGRICULTURE

Some of the most exciting aspects of biotechnology are in genetic engineering (see Chapter 9) but we must not underestimate the work of plant and animal breeders – particularly since the careful work of Gregor Mendel (1822-1884). (For further details see *Biology Advanced Studies – Genetics and Evolution*.)

There are special biotechnologies associated with animal husbandry, 'the breeding of the best from the best', such as the selection of ideal animal breeds which are most suited to our needs in any farming area. Prized stock male animals are used as sources of gametes for artificial insemination and fertilised eggs can be transferred to 'surrogate mothers' so that the high grade females can continue ovulating without 'the problem of pregnancy' intervening. These 'surrogate mothers' can be exported to other countries to establish new herds. Sperm, eggs and embryos can be stored at very low temperatures. The vets have the vaccines to protect animals from disease and the drugs to cure all manner of conditions. However we sometimes hear controversial comments about biotechnology. One such case is BST. The milk yield of cows can be greatly increased by injecting the hormone **bovine somatotrophin** (BST). This is a natural growth hormone produced by cows after calving. However the dispute is because the BST hormone now used is made by fermentation by the bacterium *E. coli* which has been engineered (see page 78) to contain the natural cow-BST gene. Some people resist this because they see it as being 'un-natural', others because there is already an excess of milk production in Europe and yet others because there has been some evidence in trials of increased stress and disease in the treated cows.

Q Consider the points for and against the statement: 'Only experts should decide because the public doesn't know enough about biotechnology to be able to make decisions on this type of issue.'

Fortunately most of the problems are less complicated to understand than this one, but are still very difficult to solve. What does a farmer do about agricultural waste? At a time when each farmer had only a few animals, they grazed his land and their wastes were recycled as fertiliser for the fields. Now with huge pig and cattle units it is difficult to dispose of the faeces and urine – and the strong liquid waste from silage (grass stored as winter food for farm animals). Is there a biotechnological answer to this?

One abattoir was faced with a different type of problem in the mid 1980s. With regulations following the discovery of BSE (the 'mad cow' disease) they were unable to sell animal residues as before and even had to pay to have these wastes taken away – a double financial blow. However, a local engineering company built, on the farm, a 105 cubic metre digestion system. The organic material is biodegraded by bacteria under anaerobic conditions. Biogas is made in quantities sufficient to run the system and provide hot water and steam for the abattoir; the liquid waste is pumped onto the fields and the solid residue composted and sold to local farmers at £80 per tonne. A neat biotechnological answer – and this system has now been adopted by 10% of abattoirs in the UK.

■ Pharming

This rather coy term (for a blend of pharmacy and farming) refers to one of the most profitable of agricultural biotechnologies. It depends on the transfer of a gene from one species (perhaps human) into another (a farm animal, such as a sheep) so that the human gene may be expressed in some form such as a protein in the milk of the sheep. This **transgenic** process has already had some success and many 'pharmed' products may be seen in the future. (See page 82.)

Transgenic lambs in a feeding pen

■ Plants

Most of the techniques used in plant biotechnology depend on DNA and gene transfer (see Chapter 9). There has been a long search for the nitrogen–fixing gene of the bacterium *Rhizobium* found in root nodules of leguminous plants (see the organism file on page 30). If it could be isolated and transferred into cereal crop plants, they would be able to fix their own nitrogen from the air. This would cut the cost of fertilisers and reduce the pollution of water courses caused by excessive fertiliser run-off from agricultural land. In fact, we now realise that not one but 17 genes are involved in the nitrogen-fixing sequence and new techniques will be needed to insert them as a complete package. (See the scientist file on page 81.) At present, the commercially important plant biotechnology methods of micropropagation and

cloning result in the production of many plants which are exact genetic copies of the original. They are grown in tissue culture under sterile conditions and with subtle variations of nutrient and hormone concentration. Many ornamental plants are now grown in this way.

Perhaps the most amazing technique is the growth of complete plants from single cells. A small piece of plant tissue is treated with enzymes that separate the cells and remove the cellulose cell wall. The resulting naked **protoplasts** can each be cultured, in the right conditions, to form a small cluster of cells, a **callus**. The callus cells are grown on by tissue culture techniques into complete plants. This is an expensive but effective way of rapidly producing a large population of plants from one valuable plant, making possible the marketing of huge numbers of genetically identical high value plants. The protoplasts of closely related plants can be fused to give hybrids (page 126).

Q 1. Figure 8.3 shows different stages in the treatment of water.
Identify *three* stages in which microorganisms are involved and for each stage describe the involvement.

Q 2. Describe how you would use an autoclave or pressure cooker to sterilise 10 cm^3 of a nutrient culture solution.

Q 3. Distinguish between each member of the following pairs.
(a) Antibiotics and antiseptics
(b) Sterilisation and pasteurisation
(c) Active and passive immunity

Q 4. (a) Draw a large labelled diagram to show the structure of a single cell of *Escherichia*.
(b) Give *three* ways in which the human immunodeficiency virus (HIV) is different from *Escherichia*.
(London, A-Level Human Biology, 1990.)

Q 5. Figure 8.4 shows a sewage treatment plant.
(a) (i) Suggest the function of the screens at A.
   (ii) Outline the bacterial processes occurring at B, C and D.
(b) (i) What passes from D to E?
   (ii) What may happen to the sludge when it is removed from the treatment plant?
(London, AS, 1987.)

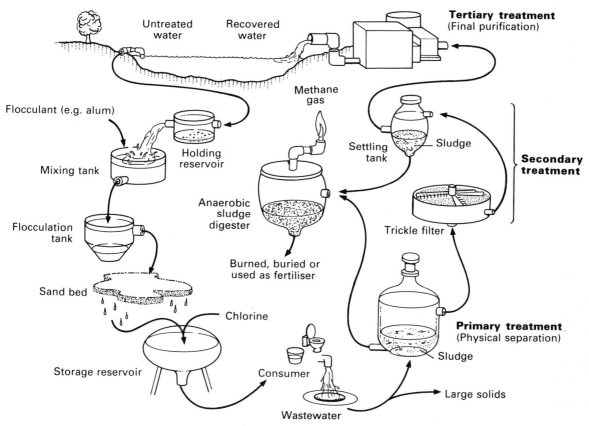

Figure 8.3 Different stages in the treatment of water

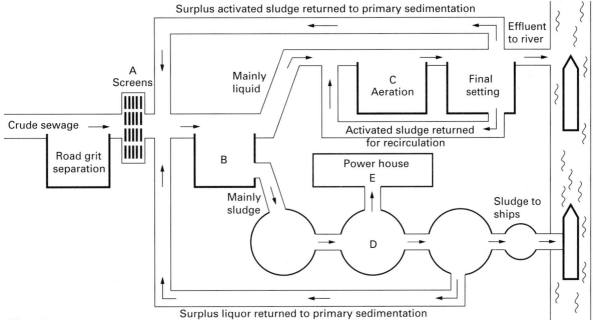

Figure 8.4

DNA BIOTECHNOLOGY

CHAPTER 9

■ 1953 to 1995 - A calendar of events

1953 James Watson* and Francis Crick* published in *Nature* '... we wish to propose a structure for ... DNA'.

1960 Discovery of messenger RNA.

1961 Francois Jacob* and Jacques Monod* announce 'operon' gene model.

1966 Khorana* and Nirenberg* discover rules of DNA coding of amino acids.

1967 DNA ligase discovered.

1970 The first restriction enzymes for cutting DNA at specific positions found by Arber*, Nathans* and Hamilton Smith*. Also reverse transcription RNA → DNA (Baltimore* and Temin*).

1973 Hybrid DNA (Berg*) and plasmid splicing in *E. coli* (Cohen).

1975 Sanger* (at Cambridge) and Gilbert* (Harvard) develop technique for rapid sequencing of DNA.

1977 First engineered bacteria to make human hormone – somatostatin.

1983 Transgenic mice - giant mice with gene for rat growth hormone. Also DNA marker for Huntington's disease gene. Also polymerase chain reaction for making multiple copies of DNA.

1985 Alec Jeffreys (Leicester) develops technique of genetic fingerprinting.

1987 Field trials of genetically modified potatoes.

1988 First patented 'OncoMouse' with human cancer-causing gene.

1989 Cystic fibrosis gene cloned and sequenced.

1993 Huntington's disease gene identified.

1994 Genes for one type of breast cancer found.

1995 On sale in UK shops, bread and cheese made by genetically manipulated organisms.

[* = Nobel prize winner]

It seems scarcely possible that within 40 years of the discovery of the structure of DNA we can now talk of listing the whole DNA code of an organism, of changing parts of the molecule, of transferring genes from one organism to another and of using bacteria, mice, pigs and sheep to make some of the human proteins missing in sufferers of genetic diseases and also of cloning genes from long-dead or even extinct organisms. If the last culture of smallpox virus were to be destroyed (see page 21) we would still have the complete genome code to make it again. Some of the events in the 40-year calendar will be explained in this chapter but the background genetics and biochemistry are to be found in two other books in the *Biology Advanced Studies* series – *Genetics and Evolution* and *Biochemistry*.

■ The double helix

The famous 1953 report in which James Watson and Francis Crick suggested to the scientific world the now accepted structure of **deoxyribonucleic acid**, gave the first view of a huge molecule built in the form of a double helix (Fig. 9.1). Although composed of only six different chemical groups (the sugar deoxyribose, the phosphate group and the four nitrogen containing bases – adenine, guanine, cytosine and thymine), DNA is able to replicate, convert its information to the useable RNA form and by means of its very simple and universal code supply the instructions for building proteins. The process is summed up in the flow diagram (Fig. 9.2) and the code table (Table 9.1).

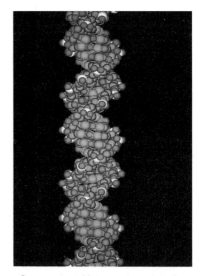

Computer graphics representation of a section of a DNA molecule

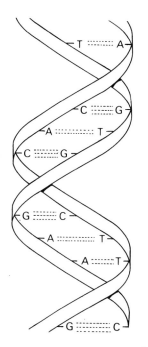

The genetic information on the DNA of a cell is known as the **genome**. It is actually the linear arrangement of all of the nitrogen bases (**nucleotides**) on one strand of the double helix. The other strand is made up by **complementary base pairing** where adenine always pairs with thymine and guanine with cytosine. The DNA remains in the nucleus but is **transcribed** into messenger ribonucleic acid (mRNA) which is single stranded and has the sugar ribose instead of deoxyribose and uracil to base pair with adenine rather than thymine. The mRNA passes through and to the ribosomes where the sequences of bases is **translated** according to the code into a sequence of amino acids. This can be summarised in a way which in the 1960s became known as the **central dogma of molecular biology**:

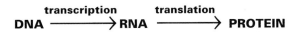

Figure 9.1 DNA structure (note the hydrogen bonding between A and T, and between G and C).

UUU	Phe	UCU	Ser	UAU	Tyr	UGU	Cys
UUC	Phe	UCC	Ser	UAC	Tyr	UGC	Cys
UUA	Leu	UCA	Ser	UAA	Terminator	UGA	Terminator
UUG	Leu	UCG	Ser	UAA	Terminator	UGG	Trp
CUU	Leu	CCU	Pro	CAU	His	CGU	Arg
CUC	Leu	CCC	Pro	CAC	His	CGC	Arg
CUA	Leu	CCA	Pro	CAA	Gln	CGA	Arg
CUG	Leu	CCG	Pro	CAG	Gln	CGG	Arg
AUU	Ile	ACU	Thr	AAU	Asn	AGU	Ser
AUC	Ile	ACC	Thr	AAC	Asn	AGC	Ser
AUA	Ile	ACA	Thr	AAA	Lys	AGA	Arg
Aug	Met	ACG	Thr	AAG	Lys	AGG	Arg
GUU	Val	GCU	Ala	GAU	Asp	GGU	Gly
GUC	Val	GCC	Ala	GAC	Asp	GGC	Gly
GUA	Val	GCA	Ala	GAA	Glu	GGA	Gly
GUG	Val	GCG	Ala	GAG	Glu	GGG	Gly

Table 9.1 The triplet genetic code on mRNA for 20 amino acids (i.e. Phe = phenylalanine, Leu = Leucine, Ile = isoleucine, Ala = alanine, etc). Note that some amino acids have more than one triplet coding for them so the code is described as being **degenerate**. Note also that in RNA there is no thymine – the nitrogen containing base uracil replaces it. There are three triplets that code for 'stop'. They cause the termination of a complete polypeptide sequence. The code AUG can either signal the start of a new molecule or the amino acid methionine (Met).

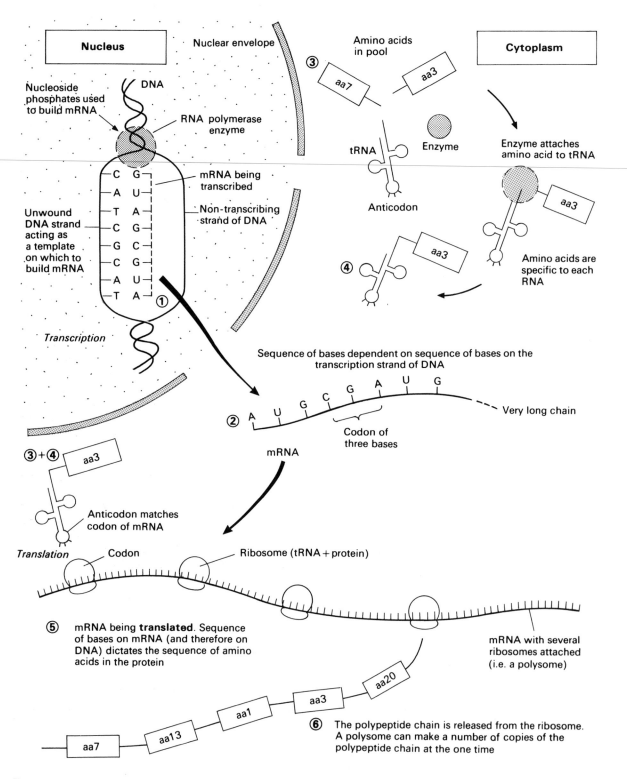

Figure 9.2 How DNA codes by way of mRNA for the production of a polypeptide (protein)

It was soon found to be not quite as simple. Not all of the DNA is used to code for polypeptides and proteins. The gene sequence is broken up by lengths of non-coding DNA known as **introns**. The lengths of coding DNA are **exons**. The first stage of transcription of DNA makes a complete transcript of primary mRNA. Then the introns are cut out, a process known as **post-transcriptional modification**. The modified functional mRNA then leaves the nucleus for the ribosomes – the sites of protein manufacture (see Fig. 9.3).

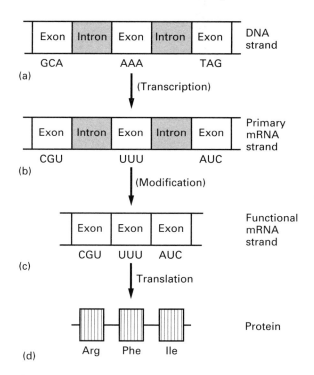

Figure 9.3 From a part of a split gene (a) with three exons (each of which is shown here with only one codon) through the processes of transcription and modification to the expression of the gene in the manufacture of part of the protein (d) which is three amino acids long.

A few facts will reveal the magnitude of the problems in molecular biology awaiting solution. There are 23 pairs of chromosomes in human body cells. They are believed to carry about 100 000 genes and the genome code is probably written in about three billion bases. It is hardly surprising that there are sometimes faults in replication, transcription and translation. Some of these faults are mutations.

Q The length of the uncoiled DNA molecules of each human cell is about 1.5 metres. What could you assume about the ratio of introns to exons?

■ GENETIC ENGINEERING or RECOMBINANT DNA TECHNOLOGY

As soon as it was realised that the genetic code is comparatively simple, scientists looked for genetic differences between individuals. They sought the sites of possible changes and tried to relate molecular differences in the DNA to changes in the proteins that could be made and so account for different physiology and in some cases deformities and disease. Attention soon turned to the possibility of removing or replacing 'defective genes'. The manipulation of genes (which is what we mean by the term genetic engineering) became possible with the discovery of two types of enzymes:
• **restriction endonucleases** which cut DNA into pieces and
• **DNA ligase** which joins together DNA molecules.

The restriction enzymes were found in bacteria. Their normal *in vivo* function is to protect the bacterial cell when invaded by viruses (or bacteriophages). They do this by cutting the foreign DNA at unique sequences of the code. Obviously the bacterial enzyme only cuts sequences that are **not** present in its own DNA. The ability of the bacteria to distinguish 'non-self' DNA *restricts* the phage growth in the bacterial cell. The first restriction enzyme was found in *E. coli* and was named (as were subsequently discovered ones) after the producing bacterium Eco RI (i.e. *E. coli* restriction enzyme number 1). It cuts DNA wherever the sequence –GAATTC– is found (see Fig. 9.4). Now, the interesting thing about this enzyme is that the cut is not straight across, but staggered with unpaired bases at each end – hence the term 'sticky ends'. Note also that the unmatched bases at the cut ends are palindromic (i.e. –TTAA and –AATT). Other restriction enzymes have different properties (see Table 9.2).

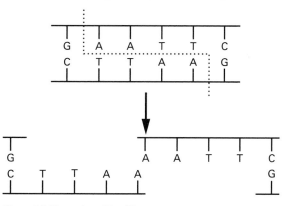

Figure 9.4 The action of Eco RI

Bacteria	Enzyme	Target sequence
Escherichia coli	Eco RI	G*A A T T C C T T A A*G
Bacillus amyloliquefaciens	BAM HI	G*G A T C C C C T A G*G
Haemophilus parainfluenzi	Hpa II	C*C G G G G C*C
Arthrobacter luteus	Alu I	A G*C T T C*G A
Haemophilus aegyptius	Hae III	G G*C C C C*G G

Table 9.2 Table of some restriction enzymes. Cleavage points shown by *.
Note that the first three cut with staggered ends, the other two with blunt ends.

After the restriction enzyme has made the cut, the sticky ends can rejoin and the join can be sealed by the action of the enzyme DNA ligase which is present in all cells.

Armed with restriction enzymes and ligase the way was open for the start of genetic engineering. By trial and error the DNA of one organism could be cut with a restriction enzyme. If the DNA of another organism was cut with the same restriction enzyme and the fragments of both mixed together *in vitro*, in the presence of ligase, it may be expected that some cut ends would come together, joining fragments from the two organisms into a **recombinant DNA**.

■ GETTING GENES INTO BACTERIA

For reasons that will become obvious, it was important that a way should be found to transfer genes from one species into bacteria. *E. coli* had been well studied and was the earliest organism to be used in this way. It is a suitable model to work with because, as a prokaryote, its DNA is in one single circular chromosome with four million bases in each strand (i.e. the full DNA content is described as 4×10^6 base pairs). It also has some smaller circles of DNA double helix called **plasmids** made up of a couple of thousand base pairs. *E. coli* cells may contain dozens or even hundreds of identical plasmids. Plasmids can be removed from one bacterial cell and inserted into another by using a solution containing calcium ions. This technique can be used to get foreign genes into bacteria because plasmids can be cleaved by restriction enzymes at the same target sequences as any other DNA. The method is as follows.

1. Extract DNA from the foreign cells and cut into 'gene sized' pieces with restriction enzyme – some pieces may have the complete gene.
2. Remove plasmids from a pure line culture of *E. coli* and cleave with the same restriction enzyme so that the circle is opened.
3. Mix together the opened plasmids and the foreign DNA fragments in the presence of ligase to splice them together into recombinant plasmids. These can act as **vectors** to carry the gene into new cells.
4. Use Ca^{2+} to insert the recombinants into plasmid-free *E. coli*.
5. Culture the new bacteria so that clones are produced from each recombinant.

The whole foreign gene may be found in some of the clones so all have to be screened to find which, if any, of the batch produces the required protein. The plasmid vectors used most often are much studied and we know which genes are found on them. One plasmid, pBR322 has genes for resistance to the two antibiotics, ampicillin and tetracycline. The screening process makes use of this fact. If the new gene has been spliced into the plasmid that ends up successfully transferred into a host cell then one of the resistance genes on the plasmid may have been split. This means that it no longer works as the host cell will not have that resistance and so will not be able to grow on agar containing the antibiotic. So we can say that the plasmid vector carries selection markers to indicate if a new gene has been incorporated.

You can now see why *E. coli* is such a suitable host for foreign genes. It can also be cultured on an industrial scale. Yeast is used as a host for similar reasons. The scheme is outlined in Fig. 9.5. In this method the plasmids have acted as a **vector** and carried the foreign gene into the host cell.

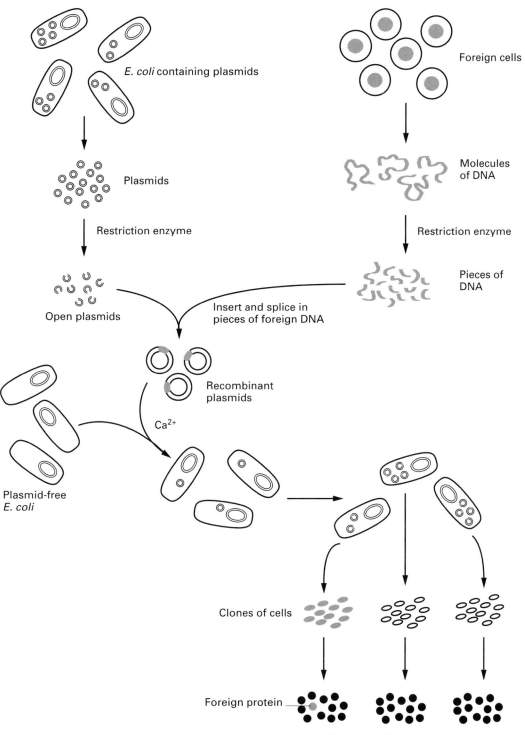

E. coli containing plasmids

Foreign cells

Plasmids

Molecules
of DNA

Restriction enzyme

Restriction enzyme

Open plasmids

Pieces of
DNA

Insert and splice in
pieces of foreign DNA

Recombinant
plasmids

Ca^{2+}

Plasmid-free
E. coli

Clones of cells

Foreign protein

Clones of cells produce proteins

Figure 9.5 Plasmids in gene technology. The plasmids are isolated from *E. coli* and different sized fragments of DNA from the foreign cells are spliced into the plasmids to make many different recombinant DNA plasmids. These are cloned and screened to find the particular recombinant needed.

There are other vector methods and it is worth mentioning four of them.

1. Use of the bacteriophage λ – a virus that infects *E. coli*, called phage λ, (λ is the Greek letter lambda). The technique used involves extraction of phage DNA, splicing into it the required gene, re-assembling the phage with its new foreign DNA and allowing it to infect *E. coli*. The resulting bacteria must be screened to find cells where the new gene is being expressed (i.e. making the required protein). Other viruses can also act as vectors.

2. Using a **tumour-inducing** bacterium. Crown gall disease is a growth of wound tissue (callus) in plants caused by the soil bacterium *Agrobacterium tumefaciens*. When it invades damaged plants, its plasmids enter the cells of the plant and carry genes for the growth of tumour (or gall) cells and also genes for enzyme production. So, *A. tumefaciens* is able naturally to get into the host cells, transfer foreign genes into the genome of the host and get them expressed in the host plant – a natural genetic engineer! Of course, we now make use of this trick by taking the tumour-inducing (T$_i$) plasmids, removing the tumour genes and inserting the gene that we wish to be carried into the plant cells. After screening, plants can be grown on by micropropagation (see page 72) and tissue culture.

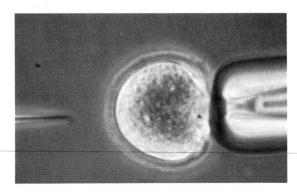

Scientist using a technique called microinjection to introduce foreign DNA into the genetic make-up of a cell. The work is done through a light microscope and visualised on a VDU screen. The circular cell is stabilised by a suction tube (right) while the probe on the left introduces the genetic material.

■ DOING IT IN REVERSE

It may have occurred to you that some of these techniques sound rather hit-or-miss. There is also the problem of the recombinants carrying a lot of extra intron material. It would solve a number of problems if the modification of the nucleic acids could already have occurred. Another enzyme reaction was found to get around the problem. Imagine a group of cells whose function it is to make one protein (perhaps the cells in a calf's stomach making rennin). They will be responding to the RNA which has already gone through the post-transcriptional modification. The functional mRNA will be present in large quantities in the cytoplasm. If this mRNA is extracted it can be mixed with the unusual enzyme **reverse transcriptase** and the reverse of the 'central dogma' happens. The mRNA makes complementary DNA (**cDNA**) and this single strand can then be used as a template to make the other helix. The cDNA (in this case the gene sequence for rennin) can be spliced into a plasmid which, within *E. coli*, is then able to make rennin in culture solution. An interesting biotechnology – non-animal rennin produced, and many people happy that cheese can be made without killing calves.

A group of **retroviruses** have the gene reverse transcriptase too and so are able to convert their own RNA into DNA which is then inserted into the DNA of the host cell. The AIDS virus HIV and some viruses causing cancer in laboratory models work in this way.

Crown gall disease on chrysanthemum plants

3. By using a gun. **Biolistics** is the jocular term applied to this vector technique that combines ballistics and biology. In 1987 it was shown the tungsten particles could be coated with DNA and fired by gunpowder at high velocity into onion cells. The foreign genes were expressed in the host cells. Particle accelerators have also been used to shoot DNA coated gold into embryo rice cells and in 1992 genetically engineered resistant wheat plants were produced by biolistics techniques.

4. By microinjection directly into the nucleus.

SCIENTIST FILE

Dr Rosi Waterhouse – Long Ashton Research Station, Bristol

After leaving school I worked in hospital laboratories and gained the qualification to enter Nottingham University to read Agricultural Biochemistry. For my PhD I then went to Durham University to research the expression of plant genes involved in the storage of proteins in peas. This led to a research post at Aberdeen University investigating plant-microbe interactions.

I was studying a newly recognised phenomenon – artificially induced symbiosis between bacteria and higher plants. It was shown that 'L-form' bacteria (i.e. a form without a cell wall) could enter plant cells and that their presence was tolerated and benign. This was a very unusual observation because it was known that even pathogenic bacteria are normally prevented from entering plant cells because of their relatively large size. The discovery of these intracellular reactions challenged the current views on the nature of symbiosis and suggested a mechanism by which sub-cellular organelles (mitochondria and chloroplasts) evolved millions of years ago (see *Biology Advanced Studies – Biochemistry*). Perhaps future exploitation of the cell-wall-less L-form bacterial associations will be used to transfer polygenic bacterial systems (such as entire metabolic pathways) into agriculturally important crop plants. In this work I had to identify gene probes and carry out DNA fingerprinting of bacteria. I then worked on an intriguing problem as a member of a team investigating the possible risks involved in the release to the environment of genetically engineered microorganisms. I had to find a very sensitive way of detecting the presence of microbes. There are several 'reporter genes' that are currently used to tag microorganisms so that they can be subsequently detected in a foreign environment

(in soil or on plants) – but I decided to use the luciferase gene. The light-producing enzyme, luciferase (found in the firefly and bioluminescent marine bacteria), is made by a gene which can be cloned. We were able to genetically engineer bacteria so that with this gene they became bioluminescent. We were able to detect the light from even a single bacterium. The work developed and was used to study pathogenic microbial colonisation of plants, long-term survival of bacteria in soil and the colonisation during a non-pathogenic L-form bacteria-plant association.

I now work on the cloning of genes involved in nitrogen assimilation. We need to know more about this because, in crop plants, the available nitrogen supply is frequently rate-limiting for growth and can result in decreased crop yields. Also there is the water pollution problem resulting from excess nitrogen (nitrate or ammonium) fertilisers being added to the soil. We have cloned several of the genes involved in nitrogen metabolism and can use 'anti-sense RNA technique' (see page 86) to genetically engineer and manipulate their expression. We should then be able to inhibit different stages in the metabolic pathway and determine the priorities that the plant makes during plant growth and development. My other approach is to engineer the plant to express luciferase. Light production will thus mimic different metabolic stages of the pathway and bioluminescence will show us how the different genes interact during nitrogen assimilation.

I am most excited by the idea that scientists can, by genetic manipulation, alter a plant's characteristics in a highly specific manner either to meet new consumer requirements or to improve agricultural efficiency. The use of the luciferase reporter gene is enabling, for the first time, the detailed assessment of natural microbial ecology, the survival of microbes in soil, in river water, on plants and as contaminants of food. I believe that a career in molecular biology as a research scientist is challenging and relevant to today's problems. There is more collaborative research so there are more chances for scientists to work in foreign countries. I had the opportunity to work for a year in Japan, cloning genes from the soybean and azuki bean.

■ GENE TRANSFER

There are now many examples of the successful transfer of one gene into a different bacterial species, (such as the rennin gene example). It is possible to isolate a gene for resistance to a chemical herbicide and insert it into the DNA of a crop plant. If the farmer plants that recombinant variety he could spray the whole field with the matching herbicide and only the crop plant would be unaffected. Another interesting example is of the potato, tobacco and cotton plants engineered to make their own insecticides. They were supplied with a gene from the bacterium *Bacillus thuringiensis* that makes a substance toxic to caterpillars. The result: the bacterial gene is expressed in the leaves of the crop plant and the toxin kills the insect pests.

An early search was made to find 'the nitrogen fixing gene'. It was thought that if cereal plants were able to fix nitrogen (like peas and beans – the leguminous plants) there would be great cost savings. However we now realise that there is a sequence of genes involved and the problem of getting them all to be expressed at the right time in a cereal plant has so far proved to be too difficult.

■ HUMAN GENES

Transferring human genes into microbes has achieved a high level of success in several well publicised examples of pharmaceutical proteins. Conditions such as diabetes, which is caused by the inability of the individual to produce a particular protein, can be treated if a suitable supply of the protein is available. Insulin for diabetics was at first obtained from cadavers (as was human growth hormone) and then from tissues of other animals (cattle and pigs). Now we have *human* insulin that is made by genetically engineered bacteria that have the human gene inserted. There have been some problems with purity and stability but these have been overcome for most patients.

Genetically engineered factor VIII became available in 1993. Factor VIII is essential for blood clotting. A mutation in the gene governing its manufacture means that the person cannot make this factor and so suffers from haemophilia A. The slightest injury to the sufferer can cause fatal bleeding.

Supplying a person with factor VIII or insulin or growth hormone does not cure the complaint, it just treats the symptoms. No change is made to the genotype of the afflicted person. Possibly in the future the techniques will be available to genetically engineer cells with the information and insert the functional gene into the host cells. Perhaps the answer will be to use a retrovirus as a vector. The expectation is that the effects of this form of therapy would decrease in time and that the therapy would need to be repeated at intervals. The gametes of the individual would not be changed and the 'defective' gene would still be passed on to offspring.

Q Discuss the possible evolutionary effects of this.

There is a strong ethical objection at present to making changes in the human genome. But what about putting human genes into other species? This is usually called **transgenics**.

■ HOW TRANSGENICS ARE FORMED – AND THE £700 'PINTA'

A transgenic organism is an animal that contains a gene of another species. The term is not usually used for plants and bacteria that have been engineered. Foreign genes have been transferred into many animals, although the usual laboratory model has been the mouse. After an *in vitro* fertilisation but before the fusion of the nuclei, the new gene is inserted into the male gamete by a micro-pipette less than a thousandth of a millimetre thick (see the photograph on page 80) and the recombination zygotes are placed in the oviduct of the mother. When the young animals are born they are screened to see if they carry the new gene. Transgenic sheep have been produced recently and have been proved to be valuable. The reason is that the cells of the mammary gland of ewes give a high yield of protein and if engineered could produce unusual proteins in the milk. A protein, alpha-1-antitrypsin normally protects human lungs from infection. Some people suffer from emphysema because they are unable to synthesise it, so they were treated with the protein which was obtained from human blood.

However the demand is now high and new methods of production are needed. The gene was isolated from human cells, micro-injected into the fertilised eggs of sheep and a small flock of transgenic sheep resulted (one ram and four ewes).

They all carried the gene and the milk of the ewes contained 30 g alpha-1-antitrypsin per litre. This milk is used as a source of the pharmaceutical protein and one litre is worth £700. It has been estimated that a flock of 2000 ewes could satisfy all of the world's demand for alpha-1-antitrypsin. (But note the discussion in Chapter 12.)

Another blood clotting protein, factor IX is isolated from milk from another group of transgenic sheep. This genetic engineering is nicknamed 'pharming' (see Chapter 8).

Some controversial ideas have also been proposed – chickens and fish with additional growth hormone genes (the 'Supermouse' has been around since 1983) and the 'OncoMouse'. Patented in Harvard University, the OncoMouse has had human cancer genes inserted. It develops tumours within about three months and can be used in researching treatments for human cancer (i.e. a **scientific model**). This is reconsidered in Chapter 12.

Mouse and 'Supermouse' – these two 24-week-old sisters from the same litter illustrate genetic engineering. The one on the right has the human growth hormone gene and weighs twice as much as her normal sister.

■ GENE THERAPY

We have already discussed replacing, in people, the proteins lacking because of a defective gene (as in the administration of human growth hormone to people of restricted growth). If the normal gene could be isolated it may be possible to insert it into functioning cells to be expressed where it is needed for the proper functioning of the individual. The first successful gene therapy treatment occurred in 1990 when a seriously ill four-year-old girl, living inside a protective plastic bubble, was treated. She was suffering from SCID (severe combined immune deficiency). She couldn't come into contact with other people because she was unable to make the enzyme ADA (adenosine deaminase) and had no immunity. Some of her white cells were removed and by means of a vector the normal ADA was inserted into their chromosomes. The cells were put back into her blood where they manufactured ADA. The girl now attends school and enjoys good health but requires regular replacement therapy. Similar studies in somatic cell gene therapy (i.e. cells other than gametes) have included malignant melanoma, muscular dystrophy and cystic fibrosis. The techniques often involve bone marrow cells. Perhaps success is near for research into some of these conditions. In the DNA 40-year calendar a year is a long time!

■ THE HUMAN GENOME PROJECT

The Human Genome Organisation (HUGO) was set up in 1990 to co-ordinate the work of scientists in a number of countries – currently the USA, Japan, UK, France, Germany, Canada, Israel, Russia, Italy and others – in a project to map all of the genes on the human chromosomes. We can still only estimate that there are between 50 000 and 100 000 genes and we know the position and structure of just a few thousand of them. Only 5% of DNA is in the genes; 95% of the total amount of DNA appears to be non-functioning and we dismiss it as 'junk DNA' – it may prove to be much more important than that.

Mapping genes and sequencing the bases of the triplet codons of DNA must have seemed an impossible task less than a decade ago and now we talk of completing it in a few decades and at a cost of $4 billion.

The automated sequencing laboratory at Genethon, Paris

The first part of the task is to chop up the DNA into pieces that can be handled in the laboratory. Restriction enzymes are used and the segments are cloned by the PCR method (see page 86). The fragments are saved in a 'genomic DNA library' and then each fragment is cut by further enzymes and the sequence of the bases identified. The methods change rapidly; at first it was done by radioactive tracer techniques, then by fluorescent labelling and now by automated sequencing machines. Dr Liz Evans, the Director of the European Office of HUGO, recently estimated that 'if 500 of these machines sequencing 2000 codons a day and running for 250 days per year (were used) it would still take 12 years to sequence the human genome'. Some scientists are patenting the sequences that they discover.

Q Discuss at this point whether you think that the structure of human DNA should be patented. Do you consider the cost of the project to be justified? What sort of benefits do you think might be achieved? Can you anticipate any ethical issues that may have to be resolved?

■ FINGERPRINTING AND PROFILING

Forensic science gained an effective technique in 1984 when Professor Alec Jeffreys at Leicester University demonstrated how DNA from cell samples (such as blood, skin, hair roots and semen) could be made to show an individual profile. The method is **DNA profiling** but instantly became more generally known as **DNA finger-printing**. In 1987 forensic history was made when a rapist was convicted in Bristol because the DNA of his blood sample was identical to that in some semen stains. In 1988 the Leicester police were able to convict a murderer on genetic fingerprinting evidence. Jeffreys's method is to use restriction enzymes to cut the DNA of cellular samples. You will recall that 95% of the DNA is the 'junk' part, and in those regions are short repeated sequences (about 40 base pairs long repeated up to 100 times) which vary in unrelated people. These are known as **hypervariable regions** and they are separated by restriction enzymes into fragments. The prepared DNA sample is placed on a gel in an electric field (**gel electrophoresis**). The fragments move along the gel and, because the smaller ones move further, they separate out into what looks like a bar-code. By using a method known as **Southern blotting**, the image of the bar-code can be transferred to X-ray film (see Fig. 9.6).

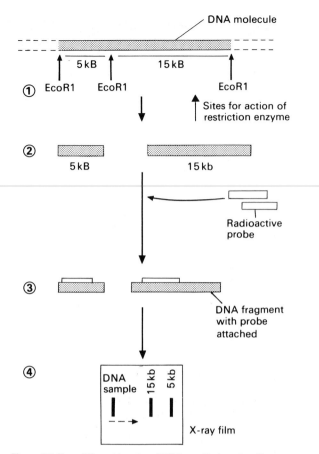

Figure 9.6 How different lengths of DNA are displayed on X-ray film using a radioactive DNA probe

The technique has now been cited as evidence in thousands of criminal cases around the world. There have been some legal challenges based either on the interpretations of the statistics or because tests were not properly carried out. However, the technique itself is very reliable and has been used even more frequently in paternity cases.

Any tissue from which DNA can be extracted can be analysed by DNA fingerprinting – even though the organism may have been dead for some time, or, in some cases, if it is now extinct . It has been used to identify stolen parrots, promiscuous behaviour in swallows, human remains, relationships between different species of grasses, pedigrees of dogs and horses and even DNA from Egyptian mummies and prehistoric insects preserved in amber. In 1994 DNA tests of tissue from the woman who claimed for 60 years to be the Grand Duchess Anastasia, daughter of the last Russian Tsar, were compared with tissue from the Duke of Edinburgh. It was demonstrated that there was no family resemblance.

Dr Linda Tyfield - Director of Molecular Genetics Unit, Southmead Hospital, Bristol

As an undergraduate at the University of Toronto, I was interested in a branch of biochemistry that dealt with 'inborn errors of metabolism' – diseases which are inherited and affect some individuals by blocking a specific metabolic pathway. My own particular interest was in Phenylketonuria (PKU), the most common disorder of amino acid metabolism. About one infant in 10 000 in England is affected by this autosomal recessive allele (see *Biology Advanced Studies – Genetics and Evolution*). If the condition is not diagnosed very early in life it leads to irreversible mental retardation. PKU was first described by a Norwegian doctor in 1934 and it develops because the normal breakdown of the amino acid phenylalanine to tyrosine is unable to occur. This is because of the loss of activity of the enzyme phenylalanine hydroxylase (PAH). My own research was directed to finding the biochemical and clinical effects of a high blood phenylalanine content and determining what treatment, if any, could be given to affected individuals to prevent the distressing consequences of PKU. The first successful use of a synthetic diet to lower the blood phenylalanine concentration was carried out at Birmingham Children's Hospital. It was exciting because in 1955 it prevented the mental retardation of a PKU child. Because of the success in treating this disorder, screening programmes using the 'heel prick test' have become common. These aim to test all babies in the first two weeks of life and any positively diagnosed infant is given a diet low in phenylalanine. It is pleasing to note that where the screening is done severe mental retardation, because of PKU, has been all but eradicated.

There are varying degrees of severity of PKU – that is, some children need greater dietary restriction of phenylalanine than others to maintain the blood concentration within acceptable limits. Since the PAH gene was identified in 1985, the DNA sequence has been studied and many laboratories, including my own, are looking at the distribution of mutations in PKU individuals. By April 1994 over 180 different PKU causing mutations had been defined. Some results in a complete loss in the activity of the enzyme PAH and others reduce it allowing some phenylalanine to be converted to tyrosine (but at a reduced rate). We have found that in the UK, most affected individuals carry two different mutations of the PAH gene (one having been inherited from each parent). It is anticipated that different combinations of these mutations have different quantitative effects on the enzyme activity. Much research is being directed to methods of screening for specific mutations and determining if this knowledge is sufficient to predict the severity of the disorder.

DNA sequencing and mutation analysis are valuable modern tools to provide an insight into the histories of different populations. For example, at the PAH gene there is great similarity between the populations of southern England and Denmark; between the Scots and the Irish and also between the Scots and the Norwegians. These genetic findings corroborate historians' thoughts about the migration and mixture of populations within the British Isles. Through molecular genetic analysis we are gaining insight into the origins of some mutations. (See also *Biology Advanced Studies – Human and Social Biology*.)

■ THE POLYMERASE CHAIN REACTION (PCR)

To carry out some of the forensic DNA profiling tests on minute blood stains the DNA must first be extracted and then amplified. The PCR technique can amplify one piece of DNA ten million times in an hour. It is generally believed that Kary Mullis thought of the method on a car journey. The relevant piece of DNA is identified and the two ends have short lengths of synthetic DNA attached. By heating the DNA the two complementary strands of the double helix separate. Then on cooling and with the addition of an enzyme, **DNA polymerase**, each single DNA strand has its complementary strand built on. Alternate heating and cooling doubles the amount of DNA at each cycle – hence it is a chain reaction. Mullis identified a heat-stable polymerase enzyme and the technique is now used widely.

■ SENSE AND ANTISENSE – TO END THE CHAPTER

Only one strand of the DNA double helix is transcribed into mRNA. It is known as the 'sense' strand. The other one is the 'antisense' strand. If the antisense DNA is forced to make RNA it will be antisense RNA and complementary to the normal RNA. So if the two RNA strands are mixed, they link together to make double stranded RNA. The ribosomes are unable to handle this so the gene concerned is not expressed and its protein is not manufactured at the ribosomes. Antisense RNA can be used to block genes and so inhibit enzyme processes. The best known example of this application is the prevention of over-ripening leading to mushy tomatoes. As tomatoes ripen colour and flavour develop but at the same time an enzyme, **polygalacturonidase**, is produced and breaks down cell walls. If antisense RNA to this gene is present, it blocks production of the enzyme so the tomatoes go through all of the other stages of ripening and stay firm. These tomatoes are already on sale in the United States. Do you think that they should be?

Q In some genetic engineering processes a synthetic gene is inserted into a bacterial host. This is shown in the diagram below.

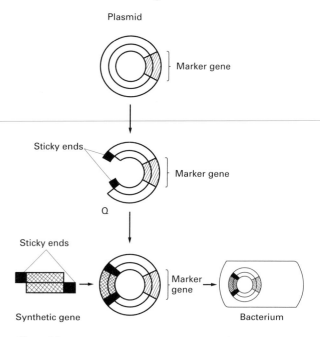

Figure 9.7

(a) (i) What term is used to describe the function of the plasmid in this process?
   (ii) Name the type of enzyme used at Q to cleave (cut) the DNA.
   (iii) Explain the role of the 'sticky ends' on the synthetic gene and the plasmid.
   (iv) Explain how the marker gene is used to recognise those bacterial cells that have been successfully transformed.

(b) In this technique, a synthetic gene has been used. Suggest one method of making a synthetic gene.

(c) Genetically engineered human insulin is now widely used in the treatment of diabetes. What are the advantages of using genetic engineering techniques in the production of human insulin?

(London, A-Level Biology 1993.)

10 MICROORGANISMS AND HEALTH

■ CASE STUDY: A KILLER RETURNS

In July 1992, dealers were ordered off the exchange floor of the World Trade Center in New York, and refused permission to return until they had taken medical tests to show they were healthy. The reason? Two of the Center's staff had developed tuberculosis. A disease from the history books had struck one of the most affluent and technologically sophisticated communities in the world.

In fact, New York's tuberculosis problem had been developing for years. Incidence of the disease had increased by nearly 150% during the 1980s, but as it had been confined mainly to the poor and the homeless it had made little impact on the public. By March 1993, however, the crisis had reached such serious proportions that the city's Public Health Department issued regulations allowing them forcibly to detain tuberculosis patients for up to two years to ensure that they completed courses of treatment against the disease: too many were giving up the medication before they were completely free of the tuberculosis bacterium, and in so doing were encouraging the development of drug-resistant strains of the organism. (This is the subject of a further case study on page 117.) In April 1993, the World Health Organisation finally declared tuberculosis a 'global emergency'.

Tuberculosis has been a major plague throughout most of human history. There are even claims that its traces have been detected in human bones from the Stone Age. In Victorian England the disease was called 'consumption', and accepted as an ever-present threat, especially to children and young adults. It even acquired a quite undeserved glamour by causing the premature deaths of romantic artists such as Charlotte Bronte, the poet Keats and the composer Chopin. By the 1950s, however, widespread vaccination and the effective treatment of infected people with antibiotics such as streptomycin, seemed to spell the end of tuberculosis as a major human problem, certainly in more developed countries. In fact, it was widely assumed then that a combination of improved vaccines, antibiotics and proper sanitation would wipe out not only tuberculosis but all important bacterial diseases within a generation or so.

So what went wrong? Why, forty years later, does tuberculosis alone still kill *three million* people every year worldwide – more than any other single cause of human death? Most of the deaths occur in less developed countries, where vaccines and antibiotics may be unaffordable luxuries; but why, if medicine in the developed world has conquered bacterial disease, is tuberculosis still considered such a threat to the affluent West that in July 1993 concern was expressed about the possible spread of the disease by air-circulating systems on jet airliners?

The answers to these questions are, inevitably, complicated, but the chapter that follows is intended to provide at least some of them. It is clear, for example, that in some areas (such as New York) tuberculosis has 'ridden on the back' of AIDS, exploiting the weakened immune systems of AIDS patients (see page 110); it is also clear that poorly planned use of antibiotics in the past has actively encouraged the appearance of drug-resistant strains of the tuberculosis bacterium (see page 117). Most importantly, however, what we learn from the tuberculosis case study is that infectious diseases have not, as yet, retired to the history books after all. In human health, microorganisms still matter.

■ THE CREDIT SIDE: NORMAL BODY FLORA

From soon after we are born, we live our whole lives in the close company of billions of microorganisms. They live on our skin, in our gut, in our nasal cavity, in virtually any body orifice, and they make up our **normal body flora**. These organisms live as *commensals*, sharing minute quantities of our food and other resources. As commensals, most of the normal flora neither harm us nor benefit us. Some, however, are known to be beneficial to health.

• The presence of the normal flora in a vulnerable part of the body may prevent disease-causing microorganisms from establishing themselves there. For example, after a girl has reached puberty her vagina is inhabited by large numbers of bacteria called *Lactobacilli*, similar to those used in the manufacture of yogurt (see page 59). These lactobacilli obtain glycogen and other carbohydrates from the cells lining the vagina, and ferment them into acids such as lactic acid. The resulting low pH of the vaginal wall makes it difficult for disease-causing organisms, such as the yeasts that cause thrush (see page 93), to become established there.

Q Vaginal thrush is sometimes treated by applying natural yogurt. How do you think this treatment works? Would any kinds of yogurt be more suitable or less suitable than others?

• It is often claimed that some of the normal gut flora produce substances such as vitamins that the human body needs but cannot make for itself. In particular, the gut bacterium *Escherichia coli* is thought to make vitamin K, a fat-soluble vitamin important in blood clotting. A problem of taking antibiotic prescriptions is that the beneficial bacteria can also be destroyed, temporarily.

■ MICROORGANISMS AND HEALTH: SOME DEFINITIONS

Endemic Describes a disease which is always present in a community, because social conditions provide no effective barriers to its spread. See *epidemic, pandemic*.

Epidemic A sudden large increase in the occurrence of a disease, either because social conditions have changed to allow its spread, or because of a change in the disease organism itself. See *endemic, pandemic*.

Facultative Able to 'switch' from one mode of life to another. A facultative parasite is able to survive and reproduce in other environments as well as the host. A facultative anaerobe is also capable of respiring aerobically. See *obligate*.

Flora In Microbiology, the community of microorganisms characteristic of a particular habitat.

Host An organism in which or on which a parasite lives.

Inductive agent The pathogen that causes a particular disease. For example, the bacterium *Salmonella typhi* is the inductive agent of typhoid. Human Immunodeficiency Virus is believed to be the inductive agent of AIDS.

Infection The process of entry of a parasite into a host, and its subsequent establishment and multiplication within the host's body.

Invasiveness The ability of a pathogenic microorganism to spread within its host's body and multiply in host tissues.

Obligate Tied to a particular mode of life. An obligate parasite is incapable of reproducing or surviving in any habitat other than the host. An obligate aerobe is incapable of respiring anaerobically, an obligate anaerobe is incapable of respiring aerobically. See *facultative*.

Parasite An organism which has its habitat in or on another (larger) organism called the host. A parasite depends on its host for food and for a suitable environment.

Pandemic An epidemic covering many countries. See *epidemic, endemic*.

Pathogen A microorganism that can cause disease.

Toxigenicity The production of *toxins* (poisonous chemicals) by microorganisms.

Virulence A measure of the ability of a pathogen to cause disease. A pathogen is described as virulent if infection with only a small number of individuals results in disease. How virulent a pathogen is depends on the extent of its *invasiveness* and/or its *toxigenicity*, both defined above.

ORGANISM FILE: *Escherichia coli*

Description: aerobic, Gram-negative rod-shaped bacterium; many different genetic strains, some of them motile by means of flagella.

Habitat: human intestinal tract.

Importance: 1. possibly an important source of vitamin K.

2. its presence in sea water or river water is used as an indicator of pollution with human faeces.

3. generally considered harmless, but causes disease in the very young or the very old (see text below).

4. important laboratory organism; source of numerous enzymes and plasmids used in genetic engineering (see page 79).

Relatives: E. coli is one of many so-called 'coliform' bacteria, all of them aerobic, Gram-negative rods; bacteriologists tell them apart mainly by their surface chemistry and the different sugars they are able to ferment.

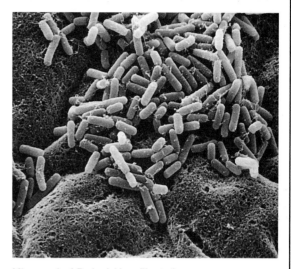

Micrograph of *Escherichia coli* bacteria on agar

■ THE DEBIT SIDE: MICROORGANISMS AND DISEASE

The word 'disease' can describe a wide range of body malfunctions, with widely differing causes: alcoholism, schizophrenia, rickets and mumps are all described as diseases, although their causes are very different. In this book, use of the word is restricted to *infectious* or *transmissible* disease. In this sense, a disease is a particular kind of host-parasite interaction, with the parasite's activities and the host's responses combining to produce a characteristic set of symptoms.

Q Find out what you can about the causes of alcoholism, schizophrenia, rickets and mumps. It is useful to call them all 'diseases'? Why is a broken leg not a disease?

To many people, all microorganisms (or 'germs') are inescapably linked with disease. Television advertisements for household disinfectants play on this idea. Even people who should know better (such as Biology students) tend to divide microorganisms, like characters in a children's story, into the 'good guys' and the 'bad guys'. The 'good guys', of course, are the microorganisms that 'help

us', such as nitrogen-fixing bacteria or those used in making yogurt; the 'bad guys' are the *pathogens* – that is, microorganisms that cause disease, either of us, or of domesticated animals, or of crop plants.

In real life (human or microbial), the distinction between 'good guys' and 'bad guys' is not always so clear-cut. For example, the enormous population of *Escherichia coli* living in your gut may help you by producing vitamins, and usually does you no harm, other than using tiny quantities of your food – as long as the bacteria stay in the gut. In the very young, the very old and those who are seriously weakened by other infections, *E. coli* may escape from the gut into the bloodstream, and from there infect other parts of the body such as the urinary tract: *E. coli* is the commonest inductive agent of urinary tract infections. If *E. coli* and the other normal gut flora escape into the body cavity (for example, by way of a burst appendix) they can cause inflammation of the lining of the body cavity (peritonitis), which is fatal unless treated.

Most of the time resident organisms like these are prevented from causing harm because:
• their numbers are kept down by body defences and by competition from other microorganisms
• they are in the 'wrong place' to cause disease, and lack the ability to spread to other parts of the body.

ORGANISM FILE: *Salmonella enteritidis*

Description: aerobic, Gram-negative rod-shaped bacterium, motile by means of flagella.

Habitat: intestinal tract of humans and other animals; commonly present in chickens and other poultry, and in their eggs.

Importance: a major cause of infective food poisoning (salmonellosis) – see page 100. The bacteria infect cells of the gut lining and produce an *endotoxin* (see text), which irritates the lining and causes violent vomiting and diarrhoea. Symptoms usually appear within 8 to 48 hours of ingesting food contaminated with *S. enteritidis*, and last for two to five days.

Salmonella food poisoning results from the following sequence of events.

1. Food for human consumption becomes contaminated with *Salmonella*. This may happen in slaughter-houses, when *Salmonella* in animal guts may be transferred to meat. Alternatively, food workers handling contaminated meat or offal may transfer the bacteria to other food items on their hands or utensils.

2. Contaminated food is left for a time at a warm temperature, allowing *Salmonella* to multiply. *Salmonella* is not a very virulent pathogen, and large numbers must be ingested if infection is to occur. If meat is frozen immediately after slaugh-ter, and cooked immediately after defrosting, *Salmonella* infection is unlikely.

3. The food is undercooked. *Salmonella* is killed at 60 °C. Many cases of *Salmonella* food poisoning result from frozen chickens, in which *Salmonella* has multiplied before freezing, being cooked before they are fully defrosted, so that the meat in the centre is only partly cooked. It is dangerous to store cooked and uncooked meat carelessly in the same refrigerator, because fluid from uncooked meat contaminated with *Salmonella* can drip onto cooked meat, which is usually eaten without further heating.

Some two million cases of *Salmonella* food poisoning occur per year in Europe. In babies or elderly people the condition can be fatal, due to the fluid and salt loss that result from the diarrhoea.

Relatives: there are lots of salmonellae, all living in animal guts, many of them capable of causing gut infections in humans. *Salmonella typhi* (see the organism file on page 101) is the inductive agent of typhoid, one of the so-called *enteric fevers* caused by certain salmonellae. Various species of *Shigella*, which are similar to salmonellae but non-motile, cause a variety of bacterial dysentries.

Only if body defences are weakened, or if some change in the body wipes out their competitors, or if they are accidentally transferred to a different part of the body, do they cause disease. Because their ability to infect depends on chance 'opportunities' of this kind, organisms like this are called *opportunistic* pathogens.

Salmonella enteritidis, by contrast, is an out-and-out pathogen (see the organism file above). In other ways, however, it is very similar to *Escherichia coli*: both are Gram-negative, flagellated rods living mainly in animal intestines. So exactly what is it that makes one of these organisms a benign, normal inhabitant of everybody's gut, and the other a dangerous pathogen?

■ WHAT MAKES A MICROORGANISM PATHOGENIC?

Firstly, a pathogen must be capable of living as a *parasite* in its host's body. Some pathogens, like the bacteria that cause leprosy, are *obligate* parasites, incapable of any other mode of life; all viruses are obligate parasites. Other pathogens, like the bacteria that cause tetanus, are *facultative* parasites, able to live parasitically and also in other ways. However, a successful parasite is not necessarily a pathogen. Many parasites live in equilibrium with their hosts, causing no detectable ill effects. A pathogen can be thought of as a badly adapted parasite, whose presence in the host disrupts the normal running of the host's body and results in the complex interaction called a disease. What brings about the disruption is usually either the pathogen's *invasiveness* or its *toxigenicity* or both. Non-pathogenic parasites lack both invasiveness and toxigenicity.

Invasiveness is the ability of a pathogen to spread through the host's body from its site of entry, to enter host tissues and to multiply there. This ability usually depends on two things.

• The pathogen must have a surface structure that protects it from phagocytosis and other host defences (see page 104). This may be in the form of a slime capsule (see Chapter 1) or of surface antigens that are shared with the host and thus not recognised by the host's immune system as foreign.

• Often, invasive pathogens secrete enzymes that catalyse the breakdown of host connective tissues and intercellular cement, enabling the pathogens to invade tissues. The bacterium *Staphylococcus aureus*, for example, produces *hyaluronidase*, an enzyme which brings about the breakdown of hyaluronic acid, a component of intercellular cement. It also produces *haemolysins*, enzymes which cause the destruction of blood cells.

Highly invasive pathogens include those which cause bubonic plague or anthrax. *Staphylococcus aureus* is a moderately invasive pathogen. However, some pathogens show almost no invasiveness at all. *Salmonella enteritidis*, for example, causes severe food poisoning when taken into the gut, but is quite incapable of spreading from the gut into the rest of the body. *Clostridium tetani*, the bacterium which causes tetanus, is usually introduced into the body in a deep cut or wound, and rarely spreads from that site. Pathogens like these cause disease solely by their toxigenicity: that is, they release chemicals (toxins) which are poisonous to the host.

Bacterial toxins can be divided into two distinct types.

• **Exotoxins** are chemicals (usually proteins) which are secreted by pathogens into their surroundings. They are inactivated by heat, or by treatment with chemicals such as ethanol, or by prolonged storage. For example, *Clostridium tetani* produces an exotoxin which affects the nervous system: see the organism file on page 92 for more details.

• **Endotoxins** are components of the cell wall of all Gram-negative bacteria. They are all lipopolysaccharides (lipid bonded to carbohydrate), and unlike exotoxins are not easily inactivated by heat. Endotoxins are not secreted, but are released when bacterial cells break up after death. Small quantities of endotoxin in the body lead to fever and activation of the immune system. In larger amounts, endotoxins cause *toxic shock*, which can rapidly lead to collapse of the circulatory system and death.

■ Fungal diseases

Our treatment of pathogenicity so far has concentrated on bacteria, but the idea of pathogens as parasites that are able to spread through the body (invasiveness) or to produce toxins (toxigenicity) applies to other microorganisms as well. Pathogenic fungi are generally invasive rather than toxigenic, and in many cases their invasiveness is restricted to the body surface, causing the so-called *superficial mycoses* such as athlete's foot. (A mycosis is a disease whose inductive agent is a fungus.) In temperate parts of the world most mycoses are fairly trivial, but in the tropics some *deep mycoses*, in which the fungal pathogen invades deep into the body, can have devastating effects (see photograph). A common and troublesome mycosis in the U.K. is *thrush* or *candidiasis*, caused by a yeast called *Candida albicans* and its close relatives. The organism file on page 93 gives the details.

Patient suffering from chromoblastomycosis (Mossy foot)

■ Protozoal diseases

Three groups of Protozoa contain members which are common pathogens of humans.

1. Various *amoebae* (Rhizopoda) can cause gut infections: for example *Entamoeba histolytica*, the inductive agent of amoebic dysentery.

2. A variety of *flagellates* (Mastigophora) cause severe tropical diseases such as sleeping sickness and Chagas' disease. The flagellate *Trichomonas vaginalis* (see Fig. 2.3 on page 12) causes trichomoniasis, a sexually transmitted disease causing irritation and inflammation of the genital tract in both sexes. There is usually a frothy yellow vaginal discharge in females and sometimes a white urethral discharge in males. In males, however, infection may produce no symptoms, and it is important that if a female is affected, her sexual partner is treated too.

ORGANISM FILE: *Clostridium tetani*

Description: Gram-positive, rod-shaped bacterium; an *obligate anaerobe*, poisoned by exposure to oxygen; in unfavourable conditions, forms large *endospores* at the end of the cell, giving a characteristic 'drumstick' appearance (see photograph). The spores are very resistant to heat and desiccation, and can survive exposure to oxygen.

Habitat: common in most soils, either as spores or as actively growing cells; found in the faeces of horses and other animals.

Importance: inductive agent of tetanus (lockjaw). Infection usually occurs by spores being carried into a deep cut or animal bite. The spores are able to germinate in dead tissue around the wound, where conditions are anaerobic: the growing bacteria produce a powerful *exotoxin* (see text), which interferes with the transmission of nerve impulses across synapses. Symptoms, which may appear a few days or a few weeks after infection, include muscular spasms and convulsions, spreading from the site of infection to the whole body. Eventually most voluntary muscles are affected, contracting and staying contracted: death from suffocation results when this affects the respiratory muscles.

Tetanus can be treated with antibiotics in the early stages of infection, and also by injecting *antitoxin*. Antitoxin is produced by injecting horses with tetanus toxin which has been inactivated with formalin or heat. The inactivated toxin is called *toxoid*, and although it does not harm the horse, the animal's immune system is stimulated to produce antibodies against it. This antitoxin is purified from horse serum, and used to treat suspected tetanus infections. Treatment with antitoxin must take place soon after the suspected infection: once tetanus toxin has 'fixed' onto nerve tissue, antitoxin treatment is ineffective.

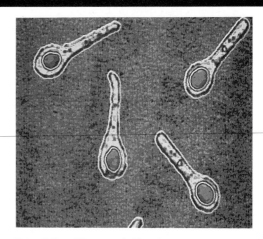

Cells of *Clostridium tetani* with endospores

Children can be immunised against tetanus by injections of toxoid in early infancy. If you have had a 'tetanus shot' since early childhood, for example after cutting yourself or being bitten by a dog, what was injected was probably horse antitoxin coupled with a dose of toxoid (a 'booster') to re-stimulate your immune system to produce your own antitoxin.

Q Because *Clostridium tetani* is common in soil, it often contaminates food and is often taken into the gut. Why does this not result in tetanus? (Clue: tetanus toxin is a protein.)

Relatives: Clostridium species are common soil saprophytes. *Clostridium botulinum* is a soil organism that sometimes contaminates canned food. In the anaerobic conditions inside the can it multiplies and releases a powerful exotoxin that causes botulism. This is often fatal.

A number of clostridia can multiply in infected wounds and cause gangrene.

---

3. The Apicomplexa are highly specialised protozoan parasites, with complex life cycles often involving two different hosts. The group includes several species of *Plasmodium*, the inductive agent of malaria. *Plasmodium* and malaria are dealt with in detail on pages 96-9.

The only ciliate protozoan known to cause disease in humans is *Balantidium coli*, the inductive agent of a rare form of dysentery. Only a few hundred cases have been recorded.

■ Viral diseases

Most pathogenic bacteria, fungi and protozoa are *extracellular* parasites: that is, they live outside living body cells, in the tissue fluids or intercellular spaces. (Tuberculosis bacteria are an exception, and so for part of their life cycle are the protozoa that cause malaria: these pathogens are described more fully on pages 117 and 96-8). Any damage that extracellular parasites cause to living cells is usually due to toxins or enzymes that they secrete.

ORGANISM FILE: *Candida albicans*

Description: a yeast-like fungus which can grow as oval budding cells or as a branching *pseudomycelium* (see diagram).

Habitat: part of the normal flora of mucous membranes in the mouth, respiratory tract and female reproductive system; normally found in small numbers, kept low by competition from other microorganisms.

Importance: inductive agent of thrush, usually in the mouth or vagina. Oral thrush shows as white patches of pseudomycelium on the mouth lining and tongue. The infection is usually restricted to the surface. Vaginal thrush usually occurs if the pH of the vaginal secretions has risen. Vaginal secretions usually have a pH of about 4, but this may rise during periods or during pregnancy, or as a result of taking the contraceptive pill. The mildly acidic pH that results (pH 6 or so) is highly favourable to the yeast. Vaginal thrush is accompanied by intense irritation and itching, and a discharge is produced. Thrush can be treated with anti-fungal chemicals such as *nystatin*, taken as a lozenge for oral thrush or as a pessary for vaginal thrush. Control is difficult, as the yeast is present in the normal flora.

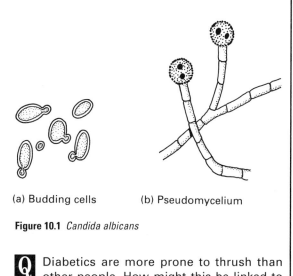

(a) Budding cells   (b) Pseudomycelium

Figure 10.1 *Candida albicans*

Q Diabetics are more prone to thrush than other people. How might this be linked to the fact their blood sugar levels are likely to vary more than those of non-diabetics?

Relatives: a related fungus (*Trichosporon*) causes 'white piedra', a disease of the beard and moustache. It is best treated by shaving!

Because they are outside living body cells, they are exposed to attack by the body's defences (phagocytes and antibodies: see Chapter 11) and also by antibiotics and other drugs we may use to combat them. Viruses, however, are pathogenic in a quite different way. Although viruses cannot move or secrete enzymes, their small size makes them highly invasive, and they are easily carried to the tissues they infect. Unlike most other pathogenic microorganisms, viruses are *intracellular* parasites: that is, they 'live', or at least replicate, inside living cells. As you saw in Chapter 3, viruses have no metabolism of their own, and rely wholly on the host cell for the molecular machinery by which they replicate. (For this reason, whether or not viruses are 'alive' in the usual sense of the word is highly debatable). The symptoms of a viral disease usually result from cell death and tissue damage as replicated viruses are released from infected cells, and from host responses to such damage. For example, the viruses that cause the common cold (rhinoviruses) infect the mucous lining of the nasal cavity, which is damaged by their replication. In response, the mucous membrane becomes inflamed and irritated, and over-produces mucus, resulting in the familiar symptoms of a cold.

A characteristic of some viral infections is *latency*. After the initial infection, when symptoms have come and gone, the viral DNA remains integrated in the DNA of host cells, and is able to be activated on future occasions. Herpes simplex type 1 is a common human virus giving latent infections: details are given in the organism file on page 22.

Because antibiotics and other anti-microbial drugs exert their effects by interfering with microbial metabolism, they have no effect on viruses, which have no metabolism outside living cells. This means that most of the common *endemic* diseases of developed countries are viral in origin, such as the common cold, influenza, mumps, measles and chickenpox. It also means that these and more serious viral diseases, such as hepatitis and AIDS, are difficult or impossible to treat and cure. Control of viral diseases is therefore exercised mainly through vaccination (page 114) and through measures to block their spread.

THE SPREAD AND CONTROL OF DISEASE

Controlling a disease is quite different from treating it. The idea of control is to prevent people from catching the disease in the first place, rather than curing them once they have. Before health organisations can begin to control a disease, they need to know two important things about it.
• What the *source of the infection* is – in other words, where the 'reservoir' of pathogens is, from which the disease enters the community.
• What the *route of transmission* is – in other words, how it reaches the patients it affects.

Sources of infection

If you catch an infectious disease, you are probably infected from one of the following sources:
• from *other infected people*. For pathogens that can live only in the human body, like the leprosy bacterium (Hansen's disease), it is the *only* source of the disease, and spread can be effectively controlled by *quarantining* infected people and limiting their contact with others. Some people may catch a disease and recover from it but remain carriers of the disease, showing no further symptoms themselves but harbouring the pathogen in their bodies and often excreting it into their surroundings. About three percent of people who recover from typhoid become carriers, harbouring the bacteria in their gall bladders and excreting them for many years.
• from *infected animals*. Many human pathogens also infect other animals. A disease such as this is called a *zoonosis*. Zoonoses may be more difficult to control than diseases that affect humans only, as natural animal populations can act as a huge reservoir of pathogens for future infection. Yellow fever and rabies are both important zoonoses.
• from the *non-living environment*, especially soil and water. A number of soil saprophytes, such as *Clostridium tetani*, are also opportunistic pathogens. An injury caused by, for example, a gardening implement can allow such organisms into the body and cause infection.

Routes of transmission

Diseases may spread through human populations in the following ways.
• *Contagious* diseases are caught by direct contact with infected individuals. This may be skin-to-skin contact, or pathogens may be present in *body fluids* passed from one individual to another (including blood, mucus, saliva, semen and vaginal secretions).
• *Airborne* or *droplet* infections are passed on when infected people breathe, cough or sneeze out tiny droplets of mucus containing pathogens: others are infected when these are breathed in.
• Pathogens may be passed from an infected person to a healthy one by an animal *vector*.
• Pathogens may be spread by ingestion of contaminated *food* or *water*.

Transmission by contact

Most of the diseases that require direct person-to-person contact for their spread are either trivial (like colds, chickenpox and mumps), or if they are life-threatening they develop slowly over a long time (like leprosy or AIDS). This is not coincidence, but the result of ordinary Darwinian natural selection. If a pathogen can be transmitted only by direct contact with infected people, natural selection will favour organisms which allow their hosts to remain active and mobile and in contact with others: only then can the pathogen be passed on. A contagious pathogen that quickly killed its hosts, or which immediately made them so seriously ill that they were bed-ridden and isolated, would soon die out through lack of opportunities for transmission.

Mumps (otherwise known as *epidemic parotitis*) is a contagious disease in the trivial category, although it can cause serious symptoms and effects. It is only known to affect humans, and is infectious from about four days before the onset of symptoms to about a week after. The virus is transmitted by direct contact, and in droplets. Details of the course of the disease are given in the organism file on page 96. The mumps virus is very similar to that causing measles, but much closer contact with an infected person is needed to transmit mumps than is required for measles.

Control of contagious diseases is attempted in two main ways:
• by *quarantining* infected people and limiting their contact with others
• by *vaccination* (see page 114).
This combination of measures has been effective in the reduction of a number of diseases, and in the case of smallpox has resulted in its complete eradication.

7m to get jab for measles

Chris Mihill, Medical Correspondent

Seven million children are to be immunised against measles in November to prevent a predicted epidemic, the Department of Health announced yesterday.

All children aged between five and 16 will be offered the injections in a £20 million programme, regardless of whether they were vaccinated as babies or have acquired protection through contracting measles.

It is estimated that without the campaign 200 000 children could develop measles next year.

Although 93 percent of children under school age have been vaccinated since 1988 with the MMR vaccine (measles/mumps/rubella), which gives all the protection they need, before this measles immunisation rates were much lower. The older measles vaccine gave 90 percent protection, so even when children did receive it 10 percent of them would not have been protected. Given these cases and the numbers in the past not immunised, the Department of Health calculates that 14 percent of secondary school children – around 1.2 million – have no protection against measles.

"Although the disease is generally mild, it tends to be less mild in older age groups."

Children will also receive vaccination against rubella. Up to 2 percent of girls and 20 percent of boys are not protected against this.

If unprotected women contract rubella during pregnancy babies can be born severely malformed. There were 23 such cases last year, compared to two in 1992.

Dr Ian Bogle, head of the British Medical Association's GP committee, said measles was not a trivial disease, as children could suffer impaired hearing and chest problems. "The prospect of a measles epidemic next year fills me with dread."

The Guardian, 27 September 1994

Q A short time after this decision to immunise with the measles and rubella vaccine, the Head of Ampleforth College announced that the boys in his school would not receive the vaccine because it had originally been grown on the tissue culture of cells from an aborted fetus, 20 years earlier. Some Muslims also objected to the use of the vaccine. However, the Catholic bishops decided that the use of the rubella vaccine would prevent even greater damage and even more aborted fetuses. Consider carefully your opinions and discuss with fellow students this type of issue.

■ Droplet infections

The distinction between contagious diseases and droplet infections is not always very clear, as many pathogens are known to be transmitted in both ways: mumps and the common cold are good examples. Like contagious diseases, droplet infections are usually either trivial or, if they are serious, are slow to develop, so allowing sufferers to stay in contact with healthy people and pass the pathogen on before they succumb. One droplet infection, tuberculosis, kills more people than any other infectious disease: a third of the entire world population is infected with the disease, and three million people per year die of it – a good indicator of the effectiveness of droplet transmission. Tuberculosis is described in detail on page 117.

As for contagious diseases, isolation of infected people and large-scale vaccination are the major control measures.

Description: RNA virus, about 175–200 nm in diameter. Consists of a central helical core of RNA and protein surrounding by a lipoprotein membrane.

Habitat: naturally present only in humans; can be grown in fertile eggs and in tissue culture. Worldwide distribution.

Importance: inductive agent of mumps. Transmitted by direct contact, and in droplets. The virus travels from the mouth through salivary ducts to the parotid glands (salivary glands in the cheeks). Here it replicates, causing the glands to become swollen and tender. From the parotid glands, viruses enter the bloodstream and are carried around the body, infecting the testes, ovaries, pancreas and brain. In 20% of infected males over 13 they cause painful inflammation of one or both testes (orchitis). Apart from this, there is no lasting tissue damage.

Because only one variety of the virus exists, a single infection gives permanent immunity. Passive immunity (see page 115) is passed from mother to fetus, so the disease is rare in young babies. However, the antibodies gained in this way are lost by the age of six months or so.

About 30–40% of infected people show no symptoms, but develop full immunity. While they harbour the virus, however, they are able to infect others.

There is no treatment for mumps, other than relief of symptoms.

Relatives: measles virus, rubella (German measles) virus.

■ Transmission by vector

In contract to contagious or droplet infections, diseases transmitted by animal vectors (such as biting insects) are often rapidly disabling or fatal. Again, this can be seen as the result of natural selection. Unlike contagious pathogens, those transmitted by vectors do not have their chances of transmission reduced if they quickly make their hosts very ill: their interests are best served by spreading and multiplying in the host's body as quickly as possible, filling his bloodstream with offspring for their vectors to suck up and carry to new hosts. In fact, disabling the host may positively help the pathogen to spread, as a disabled or unconscious host is less able to protect himself against insect bites. Of the major tropical diseases, the four biggest killers – malaria, leishmaniasis, sleeping sickness and filariasis – are all transmitted by insect bites. In cooler parts of the world biting insects are less common, but in the past bubonic plague and typhus, both transmitted by biting insects, have been major causes of death from disease in Europe.

Malaria kills between 1 and 2 million people every year, mostly in sub-Saharan Africa where it is the main cause of death among young children. It is also endemic in Central and South America, South Asia and the Far East. Four different species of the protozoan *Plasmodium* cause malaria in humans, but most deaths are caused by *malignant tertian malaria*, caused by *Plasmodium falciparum* (see the organism file on page 99). All four species are obligate parasites of humans and of mosquitoes of the genus *Anopheles*. Because only female mosquitoes feed on blood, only females can transmit malaria. The mosquito, however, is not just a passive carrier of the parasite: the sexual stage of the parasite's complex life cycle takes place in the mosquito's body, and because of this the insect is called the definitive host, humans merely the secondary host. It is normally impossible for the parasite to be transmitted without the sexual mosquito-based stage taking place (although direct transmission from human to human by contaminated blood transfusions has occurred). Like most vector-transmitted pathogens, *Plasmodium* has no effect on the health of its vector: that would, of course, be greatly to its disadvantage, making transmission to new human hosts less likely.

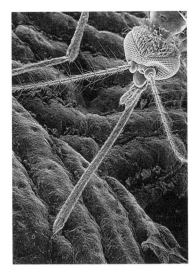

Micrograph showing the head of a female mosquito. The host skin is seen below.

Figure 10.2 Areas of the world where malaria is endemic

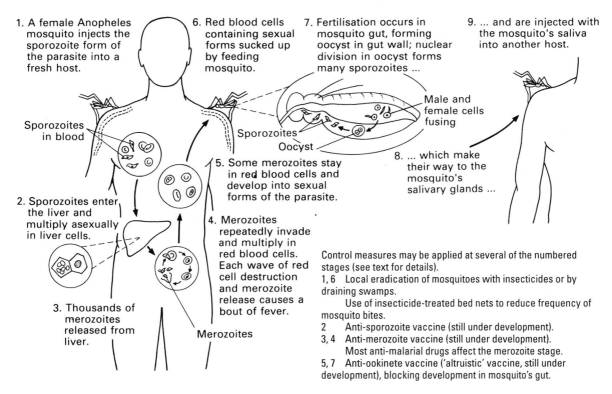

1. A female Anopheles mosquito injects the sporozoite form of the parasite into a fresh host.

6. Red blood cells containing sexual forms sucked up by feeding mosquito.

7. Fertilisation occurs in mosquito gut, forming oocyst in gut wall; nuclear division in oocyst forms many sporozoites ...

9. ... and are injected with the mosquito's saliva into another host.

Sporozoites in blood

Male and female cells fusing

Sporozoites

Oocyst

2. Sporozoites enter the liver and multiply asexually in liver cells.

5. Some merozoites stay in red blood cells and develop into sexual forms of the parasite.

8. ... which make their way to the mosquito's salivary glands ...

4. Merozoites repeatedly invade and multiply in red blood cells. Each wave of red cell destruction and merozoite release causes a bout of fever.

3. Thousands of merozoites released from liver.

Merozoites

Control measures may be applied at several of the numbered stages (see text for details).
1, 6   Local eradication of mosquitoes with insecticides or by draining swamps.
    Use of insecticide-treated bed nets to reduce frequency of mosquito bites.
2   Anti-sporozoite vaccine (still under development).
3, 4   Anti-merozoite vaccine (still under development).
    Most anti-malarial drugs affect the merozoite stage.
5, 7   Anti-ookinete vaccine ('altruistic' vaccine, still under development), blocking development in mosquito's gut.

Figure 10.3 Flow diagram of the stages in the life-cycle of *Plasmodium falciparum*

Control of malaria has been approached in three main ways:
- control of the vector
- use of drugs
- and, more recently, vaccination.

Vector control
In the 1950s the World Health Organisation planned to eradicate malaria – that is, to wipe it out completely – by the organised eradication of *Anopheles* mosquitoes from malaria areas using insecticides. In 1969 the plan was abandoned: in many areas the mosquitoes had become resistant to the insecticide (DDT), it was feared that the insecticide was too toxic to people, and (perhaps most importantly) funding from Western governments was drying up as economic problems mounted. Control of mosquitoes using DDT is now carried out only at local level. It is also possible to reduce mosquito populations by draining the swamps and marshes in which they breed, or by spraying them with surface films of oil or detergent so that mosquito larvae drown. In practice, however, the swamps are often huge and difficult to penetrate, and success has been limited.

More successful, in some parts at least, has been the use of bed nets soaked in insecticide. In one trial in The Gambia, use of such nets cut the occurrence of malaria by up to 70%.

Drugs
Quinine, extracted from the bark of the cinchona tree, is an anti-malarial drug that has been known by South American Indians for centuries. Development of more modern drugs, chloroquine and primaquine, was triggered by the exposure of American troops to malaria in the Second World War, and a similar exposure in the Vietnam war brought mefloquine and halofantrine. However, drug-resistant parasites soon arose: although mefloquine came into use only in 1985, by 1992 half of all malaria cases in Thailand were resistant to it, and with the ease of modern air travel such resistant parasites can quickly spread around the world. Development of new drugs has been slow, largely because malaria affects poor countries, and pharmaceutical companies are reluctant to undertake expensive research programmes with little prospect of getting their money back.

Where they are effective, drugs can be used both to cure people who have malaria, and as a *prophylactic* to prevent others from becoming infected. Large-scale control using drugs has been difficult, partly because the widespread use of a drug speeds up the appearance of drug-resistant parasites, and partly because it is difficult to ensure that large, scattered populations of people exposed to malaria all take it. Travellers to areas where malaria is prevalent are usually instructed to take anti-malaria drugs at regular intervals, before, during and after their visit.

Vaccination
The development of anti-malarial vaccines faces a number of major problems.
- For much of its time in the body, the parasite 'hides' inside liver cells or blood cells, protected from the immune system.
- The different stages in the parasite's life cycle (sporozoite, merozoite, etc.) all 'look different' to the immune system – that is, they have different surface chemicals (*antigens* - see page 106), so that antibodies against one stage will have no effect on another.
- The parasite has shown considerable ability to change its surface antigens by mutation; there is fear that a really effective vaccine would merely select mutant, resistant strains, which would quickly spread and become the dominant type (i.e. the evolution of resistance).

Research into anti-malarial vaccines is proceeding along three lines.
- A vaccine against proteins on the surface of the sporozoite. If successful, this would prevent infection by blocking the parasite's development after it has been injected by the mosquito. So far, trials of anti-sporozoite vaccines have had mixed results.
- A vaccine against antigens on the surface of the merozoite. This would not prevent infection, as anti-merozoite antibodies would not affect the sporozoite's infection of the liver. It might, however, prevent infection giving rise to the disease, by blocking the merozoite's entry into red blood cells. Trials in Colombia of a synthetic vaccine based on the merozoite's surface proteins have given encouraging results.
- A vaccine against the ookinete stage in the mosquito. This is called an 'altruistic' vaccine because it would not cure or protect the person who had been vaccinated, but would block transmission from an infected host by preventing the parasite's development in the mosquito's gut ('altruistic' means self-sacrificing).

No single vaccine is likely to be wholly effective in controlling malaria, but it is hoped that a combination of the above approaches might be.

ORGANISM FILE: *Plasmodium falciparum*

Description: protozoan of Class Apicomplexa; basically amoeboid, but with numerous different forms in life cycle.

Habitat: human bloodstream and liver; gut, body cavity and salivary glands of female *Anopheles* mosquitoes. Obligate parasite.

Importance: inductive agent of malignant tertian malaria. (In the following account, numbers refer to stages in the flow diagram Fig. 10.3 on page 97).

1. Infection starts when an infected female *Anopheles* mosquito bites a fresh human host and injects her saliva into the wound to prevent the blood from clotting. The saliva of an infected mosquito contains large numbers of protozoa at a stage of the parasite's life cycle called a *sporozoite*. These sporozoites make their way in the host's bloodstream to his or her liver.

2. The sporozoites enter liver cells, and develop into large cells called *schizonts*. Repeated division in each schizont produces up to 30 000 small daughter cells called *merozoites*.

3. About 10-15 days after the initial infection, huge numbers of merozoites are released from the host's liver into the bloodstream. At this stage the host will probably not have shown any symptoms, nor can he or she yet infect other people.

4. The merozoites invade red blood cells by attaching to marker substances on their surface: after a merozoite has attached, the red blood cell rapidly engulfs it. It is common for a single red cell to be infected by several merozoites. In the red cell, the merozoite digests the host's haemoglobin, using the amino acids and leaving haem as a waste product. It also causes the red cell to take in large amounts of glucose for anaerobic respiration, releasing lactic acid as a waste product.

The merozoite divides twice in the red blood cell, which then ruptures, releasing eight daughter merozoites that go on to infect new red blood cells. The periodic mass releases of merozoites into the bloodstream cause the periodic fevers that are one of malaria's hallmarks. As the parasites are released the host suffers a brief chill, followed by prolonged high fever, delirium and sweating. During the fever the merozites are invading new red blood cells. On waking after the fever, the patient feels quite well again, and remains so until the next mass break-out of parasites a few days later. During the fevers, there can be as many as 500 000 parasites in each mm^3 of blood.

5. During each cycle of merozoite multiplication and release, some of the merozoites remain in red blood cells and develop into the sexual forms called *gametocytes*. Female gametocytes continue to grow, but male cells will not develop further unless ...

6. ... they are ingested by a female *Anopheles* mosquito during a blood meal.

7. In the mosquito's gut, gametes are formed which leave the red blood cells and fuse in the gut lumen. The zygote, called an *ookinete*, burrows through the mosquito's gut wall into its body cavity. There it forms an *oocyst*, in which many nuclear divisions occur, forming thousands of sporozoites.

8. The sporozoites migrate from the mosquito's body cavity to its salivary glands ...

9. ... and are injected with the mosquito's saliva into a new host. The infection cycle is complete. If an infected person survives, malignant tertian malaria disappears of its own accord in 2–3 years. However, before this happens many patients die of kidney damage, brain damage or blockage of blood vessels caused by parasitised red blood cells sticking to each other and to capillary walls.

Relatives: Plasmodium vivax (benign tertian malaria)

   Plasmodium malariae (quartan malaria)
   Plasmodium ovale (ovale malaria)

These forms of malaria are less severe than that caused by *Plasmodium falciparum*, but last longer. Once *Plasmodium falciparum* merozoites leave the liver there is no more multiplication there, but in the other species multiplication in the liver can go on for years. *Plasmodium malariae* infections have been known to last 40 years.

■ Food and waterborne diseases

Not surprisingly, most of the diseases transmitted through food or water are gut infections, or at least start off that way. Food poisoning by *Salmonella enteritidis* has already been described (see the organism file on page 90). There is, however, a difference between food poisoning and foodborne infections. In food poisoning, the food is first contaminated with microorganisms and then stored badly, so that the microorganisms have the opportunity to multiply and reach numbers sufficient to cause trouble. The trouble may be caused by live microorganisms infecting the gut (this is *infective* food poisoning, the kind caused by *Salmonella*), or by toxins produced by the organisms while they were growing in the food (*toxic* food poisoning). In toxic food poisoning, it is not necessary to ingest any live bacteria: the accumulated toxin in the food is the sole cause of the disease. *Staphylococcus aureus* is a common cause of toxic food poisoning, producing a heat-stable exotoxin that gives sufferers violent vomiting and diarrhoea within a few hours of eating contaminated food. The illness is usually over within 24 hours.

In true foodborne infections, food is contaminated with microorganisms that cause disease without first having to grow in the food. A common cause of foodborne infection is the bacterium *Campylobacter*: there are more *Campylobacter* infections per year in the UK than those caused by *Salmonella*. Like most foodborne organisms, *Campylobacter* causes enteritis, with diarrhoea and vomiting. Many foodborne viruses are known to cause similar symptoms.

Q How do you think food poisoning and foodborne infections could best be prevented or controlled?

Waterborne diseases usually result from the contamination of drinking water with human faeces (see also Chapter 8). Some of them, such as cholera and typhoid, are still major causes of suffering and death in parts of the developing world, as they have been in the past in Europe. As you have seen, there is a link between the way a pathogen is transmitted and the severity of the disease it causes, which can be explained in terms of natural selection. (Put simply, a pathogen must not harm its host *in a way that interferes with its own transmission*. Pathogens that do not obey this rule die out and are replaced by those that do.)

Like vector-borne pathogens, those which are spread through water do not have their chances of transmission reduced by quickly spreading through the host's body and making him or her very ill. The sick person's faeces must still be disposed of, and his/her soiled clothes and bed-linen washed; and if the sewage or washing water comes into contact with other people's drinking water, transmission is assured. As the graph shows, for gut infections in general there is a clear correlation between transmission by water and the likelihood of the disease killing the patient.

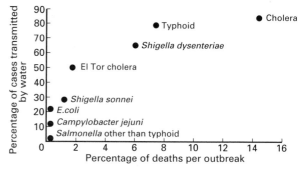

Figure 10.4 Graph showing the link between transmission by water and likelihood of death from infection

Unsanitary conditions in Calcutta, India

Control of water-borne infections is best carried out by effective sewage treatment, and purification of drinking water (see page 67). Where this is done, water-borne infections like cholera and typhoid quickly disappear.

Q In India in the 1950s and 1960s there was large-scale purification of water supplies in areas where cholera had been endemic. Where this was done, the 'classical' cholera bacterium was displaced by a less virulent variety called the EL Tor vibrio. Can you suggest an explanation for this?

ORGANISM FILE: *Salmonella typhi*

Description: aerobic, Gram-negative rod-shaped bacterium, motile by means of flagella.

Habitat: human gut, bloodstream and lymph tissue; water contaminated with human faeces.

Importance: inductive agent of typhoid. Infection usually occurs by ingestion of contaminated food or water. From the gut the bacteria enter the lymphatic system and then the bloodstream, travelling to all parts of the body. Symptoms emerge within one to three weeks, and last for several weeks. There is usually swelling and tissue damage in lymph tissue and liver, and inflammation of the gall bladder and sometimes the lungs. Bacteria in the blood cause a fever, and the patient has diarrhoea, often bloody because of damage to blood vessels in the gut wall.

Typhoid kills 5–10% of untreated patients, mainly through dehydration and salt loss. The drug chloramphenicol is an effective treatment, though resistant strains have emerged. About 3% of people who recover from typhoid continue to harbour the pathogen in their gall bladders,

intestines or (rarely) their urinary tracts. These *carriers* continue to excrete typhoid bacteria for many years, and must not be allowed to work as food handlers. Repeated large doses of penicillin or ampicillin may clear a carrier of the bacteria, but sometimes gall bladder removal is necessary.

A vaccine is available, made from whole heat-killed *Salmonella typhi* cells. It is thought to have limited effectiveness.

Relatives: Salmonella paratyphi causes paratyphoid. *Salmonella typhimurium* causes mouse typhoid: it is also a major cause of *Salmonella* food poisoning in the United States. There are many other salmonellae, all associated with gut infections of humans or other animals.

Shigella species are similar, but non-flagellated. All of them cause bacterial *dysenteries*, with abdominal cramps, bloody liquid diarrhoea and fever. *Shigella dysenteriae* is the most virulent, *Shigella sonnei* the least, with *Shigella flexneri* in between (see Fig. 10.4).

■ Zoonoses

As already explained (page 94), a zoonosis is a disease transmitted to humans from an infected animal. A zoonosis differs from a vector-transmitted disease in that the pathogen can complete its life cycle within the animal host alone, and infection of humans may be only incidental. In a vector-transmitted disease like malaria both vector and human infections are needed for the life cycle to be completed.

Because human-to-human transmission is not essential to the pathogen's survival, natural selection has placed no limits on the severity of

zoonoses in humans, and it is not surprising to find that many are very severe diseases indeed. The table on this page gives some examples.

The zoonoses in the table have been known for centuries. However, as humans encroach in greater and greater numbers on habitats such as tropical rain forests, so more and more of them come into contact with wild animals and their parasites, and new zoonoses emerge (see the organism file on page 102). One theory is that HIV began as a pathogen of African monkeys, perhaps transferred to small numbers of people in rural areas some decades ago (see page 109).

Disease	Pathogen	Host animal(s)	Mode of transmission to humans
Anthrax	Spore-forming bacterium, *Bacillus anthracis*	Cattle, sheep	Contact with infected animals or their hides
Bubonic plague	Bacterium, *Yersinia pestis*	Black rat	Bite of rat flea
Yellow fever	*Togavirus*	Monkeys	Mosquito bite
Sleeping sickness	Protozoan, *Trypanosoma brucei*	Antelope	Bite of tsetse fly
Rabies	*Rhabdovirus* (see the organism file on page 102)	Warm-blooded vertebrates	Bite or lick of infected animal; most often dogs or foxes

Table 10.1 Some important zoonoses

CASE STUDY: EBOLA VIRUS

In August 1976 a trader arrived at a mission hospital at Ebola in northern Zaire, bleeding severely from mouth and anus and in a high fever. He died within a few days, by which time half of the hospital's nurses had caught the disease. Thirty-nine people died in the hospital, and as infected patients went home the disease spread to 58 local villages. The epidemic subsided almost as quickly as it began, but by then 1000 people in Zaire and Sudan had been infected, of whom 500 had died.

The disease, previously unknown, was named African Haemorrhagic Fever, its inductive agent Ebola virus. The origin of Ebola virus is unknown, but it is almost certainly a forest zoonosis. The 1976 outbreak was probably limited by its own ferocity: a contact-transmitted pathogen that kills so many of its victims so quickly is unlikely to stay in the population for very long.

Q Explain the reasoning behind the last sentence above. How might things be different if the next outbreak of Ebola virus is of a slightly less virulent form?

Another sudden outbreak in May 1995 resulted in over 100 deaths in Zaire.

ORGANISM FILE: Rabies virus

Description: one of a family of bullet-shaped RNA viruses called *rhabdoviruses*; the 'bullet' is about 70 nm in diameter and 210 nm long, and has a lipid envelope containing glycoprotein.
Habitat: nervous system and salivary glands of warm-blooded vertebrates; most often infects bats and the dog family.
Importance: inductive agent of rabies, a fatal infection of the nervous system.

Rabies is usually caught by being bitten or licked by an infected animal. About 50% of people bitten by rabid animals develop the disease: bites on the face are the most dangerous. The virus is transmitted in the animal's saliva. Human to human transmission is virtually unknown.

The virus makes its way from the wound along sensory nerves into the central nervous system. It multiplies there, and then spreads out along nerves to the rest of the body, including the salivary glands. In humans, symptoms appear within a period ranging from two weeks to several months, earlier in children than in adults. Early symptoms include tiredness, nausea, headache and fever. Swallowing becomes difficult, leading to painful spasms of throat muscles: the avoidance of swallowing led to the disease's old name *hydrophobia*, fear of water. Finally the patient has convulsions, which lead quickly to death.

The virus's replication in the brain leads to the widespread destruction of neurones, and this is thought to account for the behavioural changes the disease brings about. Infected animals such as dogs may show 'furious rabies' or 'dumb rabies'. Animals with furious rabies become excitable and aggressive, biting other animals or humans with little or no provocation. Some also stray away from their usual range, carrying the disease with them. Animals with dumb rabies become unusually docile and affectionate, and pass on the infection by exaggerated licking.

Once symptoms have appeared there is no treatment for rabies, and it is always fatal. However, immediate vaccination of bite victims and sterilisation of the wound with antiseptic can prevent the disease from developing. The vaccine is derived from inactivated rabies virus, and is combined with the application of anti-rabies antibodies to the wound area. The viral gene coding for its outer glycoprotein has recently been genetically engineered into a harmless virus called vaccinia, to produce a vaccine which carries no danger of accidentally causing rabies.

For most of this century rabies has been excluded from the UK by strict controls on animal imports, including a six-month quarantine for imported pets without vaccintion certificates. (The length of the quarantine is necessary because of the long incubation period of the disease). This method of control has been possible only because Britain is an island. In other countries, widespread vaccination of dogs has greatly reduced incidence of rabies (notably in the USA).

DEFENCE AGAINST DISEASE

You will have realised by now that remaining free of infection is a matter of constant, and sometimes precarious, balance. Microorganisms that can cause disease are present not only in sick people, but in our everyday environments: there are bacteria in our garden soil that can give us tetanus, and even bacteria living normally within our bodies that can cause disease if they become too numerous, or if they travel from their usual habitat to some other part of the body. The fact that most of the time we remain free of disease is due to a range of defence mechanisms, some of them wholly natural, others human-assisted. We can divide these up as follows.

Natural defence mechanisms:
mechanical barriers to infection
chemical barriers to infection
reflex expulsion (sneezing, coughing, vomiting)
the immune response

Human-assisted defence mechanisms:
vaccination
anti-microbial drugs (*chemotherapy*).

■ Mechanical barriers

The *skin* is the most obvious mechanical barrier to the entry of pathogens. Over most of its surface it is dry, and the protein keratin that makes up most of the outer epidermis is tough and difficult to digest. In addition, as flakes of keratin (*squames*) are constantly shed from the outside of the skin, microorganisms are shed with them. The openings of sweat glands, hair follicles and sebaceous glands provide the most hospitable sites for bacteria, and it is here that most of our normal skin flora live. They can also provide entry points for infection: boils, for example, result from the invasion of hair follicles by bacteria called *Staphylococcus aureus*.

When the skin is broken, blood clotting, wound healing and the formation of scar tissue are important in excluding microorganisms, as well as in reducing blood loss. (For details of these processes, and of the structure and functioning of skin, see *Biology Advanced Studies – Human Systems*).

But not all of the body can be covered with tough, dry, keratinised skin. The surface of the eye and the mucous membranes lining orifices and body cavities such as the nose, mouth, respiratory system, gut and urinogenital tract, are far more inviting to microorganisms, offering moisture, warmth and dissolved organic compounds to feed on. At these sites, chemical rather than mechanical barriers are needed.

■ Chemical barriers

Stomach acid provides a barrier to the entry of pathogens into the gut. Hydrochloric acid produced by oxyntic cells in the gastric glands gives the gastric juice a pH of 2 or 3, enough to kill most microorganisms in food. However, specialist gut parasites such as the salmonellae are able to survive their passage through the stomach acid, on their way to infecting the intestine.

Lysozyme is an enzyme found in tears, and in the secretions of most mucous membranes. It is very effective at dissolving the cell walls of Gram-positive bacteria, but less effective at dissolving Gram-negative cell walls. One of the features of virulent pathogens is their apparent immunity to lysozyme.

■ Reflex expulsion

We tend to think of sneezing, coughing and vomiting as irritating or unpleasant side effects of being ill. In fact, they are defence mechanisms, triggered by the presence of pathogens or their products and having the effects of expelling them from the body. Sneezing and coughing are reflex responses triggered by irritation of the mucous lining of the nasal cavity, trachea or bronchioles. The irritation may result from microbial infection, or from some object accidentally inhaled. In either case, secretion of excess mucus and the sharp contraction of respiratory muscles expel the foreign body or bodies in a spray of fine droplets – which in the case of respiratory infections may, unfortunately, spread the infection to other people. Expulsion of microorganism from the respiratory tract is also aided by the sweeping action of *cilia* on the cells lining the tract. These send a constant current of ucus, together with trapped particles, towards the pharynx, for periodic swallowing into the acid bath of the stomach.

Irritation of the stomach lining by microorganisms or their toxic products can lead to violent contractions of the stomach wall muscles. These contractions, and simultaneous relaxation of the cardiac sphincter at the entrance to the stomach, result in vomiting. Again this has the effect of removing the irritants from the body.

■ The immune response

The immune response is a complex set of processes set in motion by the entry into the body of foreign substances, including microorganisms or their products. We can divide these processes up as follows.

• **Non-specific** immune responses are the processes that occur in much the same way regardless of what type of substance or organism has entered the body. They include **phagocytosis** and **inflammation**. The non-specific immune response has no 'memory', in that the non-specific response to repeated infections with any pathogen is always the same.

• The **specific** immune response is 'tailored' to each particular invading pathogen, and may result in lasting immunity to that pathogen after the first infection (**immunological memory**). It is the function of specialised white blood cells called B- and T-lymphocytes.

■ Non-specific immunity

The non-specific immune response is brought about by the cooperative action of several types of cell, most of them of the kind loosely called 'white blood cells' (leucocytes), although they spend as much time in the lymph and body tissues as in the blood. Table 11.1 summarises the main types of cell involved.

About 75% of white blood cells are of the kind called granulocytes, with granular cytoplasm and large, lobed nuclei, giving them their alternative name polymorphonuclear leucocytes. Most granulocytes are neutrophils, so called because they take up acidic and basic stains equally well. The small percentage of granulocytes that take up acidic stains most strongly are called eosinophils (eosin is an acidic stain that stains these cells red). The even smaller percentage of granulocytes that take up basic stains most strongly are called basophils. Basophils quickly leave the bloodstream and enter the body tissues, where they are known as mast cells.

Neutrophils are wandering phagocytes, able to leave blood capillaries by squeezing out between the cells of the capillary wall, and to travel by amoeboid movement through tissues. They are attracted by chemicals to sites of infection, where they engulf microorganisms or other foreign bodies into membrane-bound packages called phagocytic vesicles. Lysosomes in the neutrophil's cytoplasm then fuse with the vesicles, and the contents are digested by the lysosomes' batteries of enzymes.

Macrophages are also phagocytic cells. Some are wandering cells, like neutrophils, while others are fixed. Fixed macrophages are found lining passages in the lymph nodes, spleen and liver, where they make up the reticulo-endothelial system. This is effectively a filtration system. As blood or lymph passes through the passages of the reticulo-endothelial system, macrophages engulf and digest foreign particles such as bacteria or viruses. Macrophages are also found on mucous membranes and on the lining of the alveoli, again acting as phagocytes. As well as this non-specific role, macrophages are important as antigen-presenting cells in specific immunity – see below.

Monocytes form about 1% of white blood cells, and are of the kind called agranulocytes. (The other

Cell type	Location	Role in non-specific immune response
Neutrophil	Blood, lymph	Phagocytosis of foreign bodies
Macrophage	Reticulo-endothelial system (lymph nodes, spleen, liver sinusoids)	Phagocytosis of foreign bodies
Basophil (mast cell)	Blood (as basophil) Tissues (as mast cell)	Release of histamine and chemical attractants
Monocyte	Blood, lymph	Phagocytosis Secretion of complement

Table 11.1 Some of the cells involved in non-specific immunity

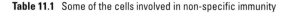

agranulocytes are lymphocytes, involved in specific immunity). They too are active phagocytes, but they also secrete a complex set of nine plasma proteins collectively called *complement*, that play a major role in activating the non-specific immune response. Liver cells also secrete complement.

The way in which phagocytic cells, mast cells and complement interact to bring about phagocytosis of invading pathogens is shown in Fig. 11.1. Neutrophils and other phagocytic cells seem to be 'blind' to invaders unless they have

been coated with a marker such as complement C3B. They also need help in locating the site of an infection, by moving up a concentration gradient of some chemical signal like complement C3A. To allow neutrophils to leave blood capillaries easily and enter infected tissues, C3A also stimulates mast cells to release *histamine*, which makes capillary walls more permeable. One consequence of this is the characteristic *inflammation* of an infected tissue. Inflamed tissues become red, swollen and hot because of increased blood flow.

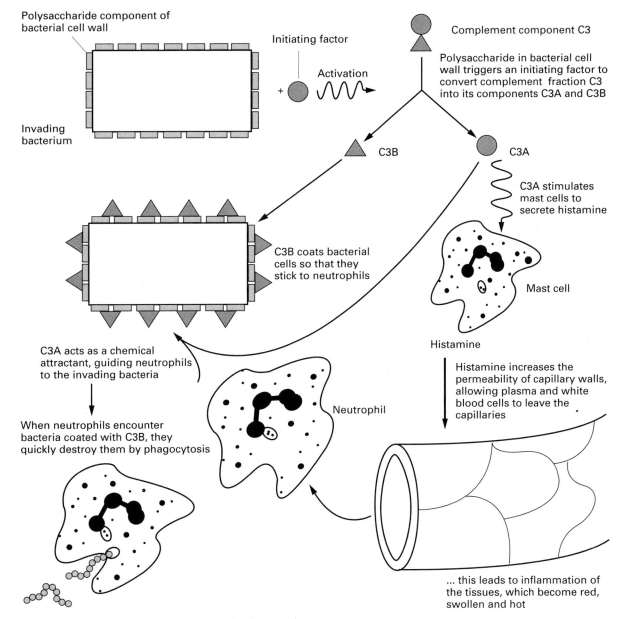

Figure 11.1 Mechanism of non-specific immunity by phagocytosis

105

■ Specific immunity

The specific immune response is brought about by the action of *lymphocytes*, which make up about 24% of circulating white blood cells. Lymphocytes develop from stem cells in bone marrow. Some of them stay to complete their development in bone marrow, and become *B-lymphocytes* (B-cells). Others migrate to the *thymus*, a mass of lymphoid tissue in the thorax of babies, and there develop into *T-lymphocytes* (T-cells).

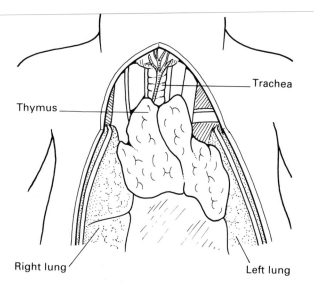

Figure 11.2 The position of the thymus in an infant. It reaches maximum size at puberty and then regresses.

The two types of lymphocyte have quite distinct functions. B-lymphocytes can secrete special proteins called **antibodies**, which act in solution against invading microorganisms or their products. This kind of immune response is called *humoral immunity*, a reference to the fact that the antimicrobial action takes place outside body cells, in body fluids – 'humour' is an old medical term for a fluid.

The other kind of specific immune response is called *cell-mediated immunity*, and involves the T-lymphocytes. Certain T-lymphocytes called *cytotoxic* or *killer* T-cells are able to identify body cells infected by intracellular pathogens (or cells which have mutated and become cancerous), and kill them by secreting toxic chemicals into them. Humoral and cell-mediated immunity clearly supplement one another: the antibodies produced in the humoral response act against microorganisms outside body cells, but are of no use against

pathogens inside cells; the exact reverse is true of the cell-mediated response. This interdependence is emphasised by the fact that both responses are assisted by the action of a second class of T-lymphocytes, the *helper T-cells*.

■ Immunological self and antigens

The immune system is triggered by the entry into the body of foreign cells or substances. Its first task, therefore, is to identify what is foreign. Lymphocytes bear on their surface receptor molecules with a specific three-dimensional shape. Any foreign molecule that fits this shape and binds to it will stimulate the lymphocyte to carry out its immune response. Any one lymphocyte (B- or T-) bears just one kind of receptor on its surface, but it is thought that altogether up to a million different receptor shapes are present on B- and T-lymphocytes in the body.

A foreign molecule that binds to a lymphocyte receptor and triggers a response is called an **antigen**. The surface chemicals of invading microorganisms usually act as antigens, but not all antigens are microbial in origin. If you have an *allergy*, chemical components of whatever it is that you are allergic to (cat fur, house dust, pollen, etc.) act as antigens, in this case triggering the immune system to 'over-react' and produce the miserable symptoms of the allergy. Nor do antigens have to come from outside the body: mutant body cells (such as those in tumours) may produce 'foreign' chemicals which act as antigens and trigger an immune response.

As well as identifying antigens as foreign, it is equally important that the immune system should recognise cells and substances that are not foreign, i.e. that are *self*. All body cells carry on their surface membrane sets of large 'marker' molecules (mostly glycoproteins), in combinations that are unique for a particular individual. The most important of these marker sets is the *major histocompatability complex* (MHC). MHC markers are the main cause of rejection of transplanted organs such as hearts and kidneys. The recipient's immune system recognises the donor's MHC markers as foreign, and killer T-cells attack the transplanted organ.

Q The structure of MHC markers is genetically determined. Why is a transplanted organ donated by a close relative less likely to be rejected than one from a complete stranger?

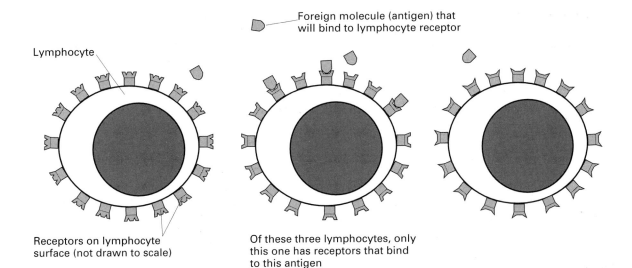

Figure 11.3 Lymphocytes, receptors and antigens

In the figure:
- Foreign molecule (antigen) that will bind to lymphocyte receptor
- Lymphocyte
- Receptors on lymphocyte surface (not drawn to scale)
- Of these three lymphocytes, only this one has receptors that bind to this antigen

It is important, of course, that a person's B- and T-lymphocytes should not carry any receptors that match his or her own MHC or other markers. It is thought that during the maturation of lymphocytes in bone marrow or thymus, any immature lymphocytes that happen to bear receptors matching 'self' molecules are eliminated.

■ Triggering the immune system: antigen recognition

Only a few specialised cell types are able to react directly to the presence of foreign materials in the body. T-cells, strangely, are 'blind' to antigens, unless they are first processed and displayed by other cells. Helper T-cells respond to antigens only when they are displayed by specialised *antigen presenting cells* (or APCs, such as macrophages). Killer T-cells, on the other hand, respond to antigens only when they are displayed on the surface of body cells *other than* antigen presenting cells. B-cells can detect and respond to 'raw' antigens, but their response is weak unless they also receive chemical signals from helper T-cells which have themselves been stimulated by antigen presenting cells.

Macrophages and other antigen presenting cells bear MHC markers of a kind called class II, (MHC-II), that are different from those of other body cells (MHC-I, class I). The surface receptors of helper T-cells are shaped so as to respond to antigen only when it is bound to class II MHC. Killer T-cells bear surface receptors which respond to antigen only when it is bound to class I MHC. This is important, because killer T-cells must treat macrophages showing foreign antigens on their surface differ-

ently from other body cells which bear antigens. Any cell which has on its surface class I MHC plus a foreign antigen must be either a body cell infected by a pathogen, or a genetically altered (mutant) cell which may grow into a malignant tumour: either way, the killer T-cell's task is to destroy it. Because macrophages and other antigen presenting cells show antigens bound to class II MHC markers, they escape destruction by killer T-cells.

The main stages of antigen recognition and the mounting of humoral and cell-mediated responses are shown in Fig. 11.4. Numbered paragraphs in the following summary correspond to numbered stages in the diagram.

1. Microorganisms, of a kind not encountered before, enter the body.
2. Some of the invading microorganisms are engulfed by macrophages and other antigen presenting cells. In the APCs' cytoplasm the phagocytic vesicles are combined with lysosomes, and the microorganisms are digested.
3. Chemical fragments of the digested microorganisms are combined with MHC-II marker molecules, and carried to the cell surface, where they are displayed.
4. Among the body's population of immature helper T-cells there will almost certainly be some whose surface receptors fit the combined three-dimensional shape of the MHC-II molecules plus the antigen fragments. The binding of MHC-II plus antigen to these cells' receptors stimulates them to multiply and to release chemical signals called lymphokines which act on B-cells. Meanwhile ...

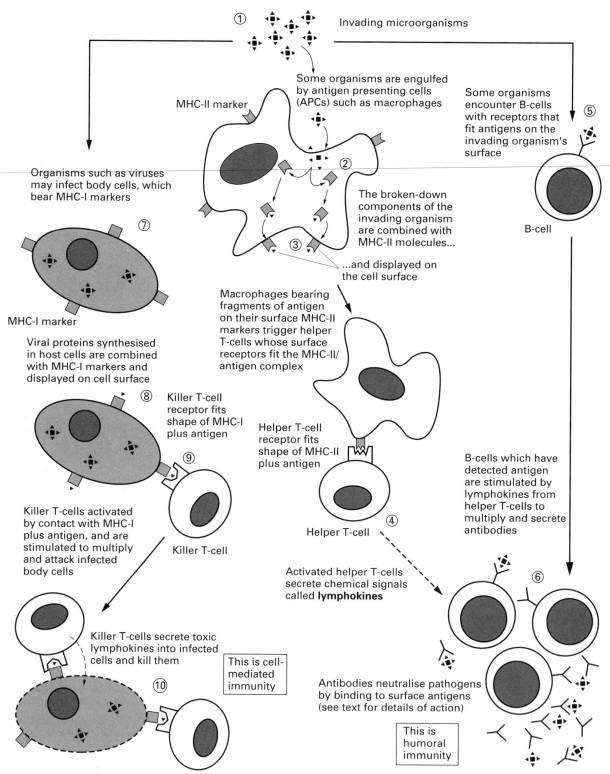

① Invading microorganisms

Some organisms are engulfed by antigen presenting cells (APCs) such as macrophages

MHC-II marker

Some organisms encounter B-cells with receptors that fit antigens on the invading organism's surface ⑤

Organisms such as viruses may infect body cells, which bear MHC-I markers

② The broken-down components of the invading organism are combined with MHC-II molecules...

③ ...and displayed on the cell surface

B-cell

⑦

MHC-I marker

Viral proteins synthesised in host cells are combined with MHC-I markers and displayed on cell surface

Macrophages bearing fragments of antigen on their surface MHC-II markers trigger helper T-cells whose surface receptors fit the MHC-II/ antigen complex

⑧ Killer T-cell receptor fits shape of MHC-I plus antigen

⑨

Helper T-cell receptor fits shape of MHC-II plus antigen

B-cells which have detected antigen are stimulated by lymphokines from helper T-cells to multiply and secrete antibodies

Killer T-cells activated by contact with MHC-I plus antigen, and are stimulated to multiply and attack infected body cells

Killer T-cell

Helper T-cell ④

Activated helper T-cells secrete chemical signals called **lymphokines**

⑥

Killer T-cells secrete toxic lymphokines into infected cells and kill them

This is cell-mediated immunity

⑩

Antibodies neutralise pathogens by binding to surface antigens (see text for details of action)

This is humoral immunity

Figure 11.4 The main stages of antigen recognition and the mounting of humoral and cell-mediated responses

5. Among the body's population of immature B-cells there will almost certainly be some whose surface receptors fit the surface antigens of the invading microorganisms.

6. The combined effect of the binding of these antigens and the lymphokines from helper T-cells stimulates this population of B-cells to multiply, mature and secrete antibodies with the same binding recognition shape as their surface receptors. These active antibody-secreting B-cells are called *plasma cells*. The antibodies combat the pathogens and/or their toxins in a number of ways (see page 106). These effects constitute **humoral immunity**.

7. Some pathogens, especially viruses, enter body cells and multiply inside them.

8. Infected body cells synthesise viral proteins as part of the virus's replication cycle. Usually, fragments of these foreign proteins are combined with MHC-I marker molecules and displayed on the surface of infected cells.

9. Among the body's population of immature killer T-cells there will almost certainly be some whose surface receptors fit the combined three-dimensional shape of the MHC-I molecules plus the fragments of the viral proteins synthesised within infected cells.

10. The binding of MHC-I plus antigen to the immature killer cells' receptors stimulates them to multiply and to mature. Mature killer T-cells will secrete toxic lymphokines into any cells they encounter whose MHC-I-plus-antigen fits their surface receptors – in this case, virus-infected body cells. This constitutes **cell-mediated immunity**.

■ AIDS and the immune system

Acquired Immune Deficiency Syndrome (AIDS) is a viral disease which seriously damages the immune system. The inductive agent of AIDS is believed to be Human Immunodeficiency Virus (HIV), described in the organism file below. A person infected with HIV may show no symptoms for years. (It may be that some HIV-positive people will never show symptoms or develop AIDS: the disease is still being researched as it is a relatively recent phenomenon.) However, the typical pattern associated with HIV infection is a slow decline in the infected person's immune system, especially in the number of helper T-cells. Eventually the patient's ability to respond to pathogens or to mutant body cells is so reduced that he or she is overwhelmed by infection or by cancerous

ORGANISM FILE: Human Immunodeficiency Virus (HIV)

Description: RNA retrovirus (see page 20). Virion consists of two molecules of RNA with associated enzymes, contained within a bullet-shaped protein core. Core surrounded by lipid bilayer with projecting glycoprotein molecules.
Habitat: human immune system.
Importance: inductive agent of AIDS (Acquired Immune Deficiency Syndrome).

Transmitted when body fluids containing either infected cells or free HIV virions are passed from one person to another. The commonest mode of transmission is sexual. Because anal intercourse is more likely to involve tissue damage and bleeding than vaginal intercourse, spread in Western countries was initially most rapid amongst male homosexuals. In recent years, however, its spread has been fastest amongst heterosexuals. Contaminated blood transfusions were a source of infection before donated blood came to be routinely screened for HIV. The virus also spreads easily on hypodermic needles shared by injecting drug abusers.

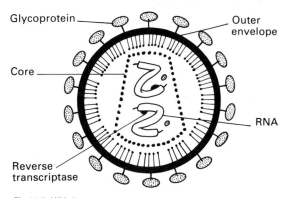

Fig.11.5 HIV virus

Once inside the body, the virus selectively infects cells carrying a particular glycoprotein receptor molecule (called CD4) on their surface membrane. These include helper T-cells, and other cells of the immune system. The cellular infection cycle is summarised in Fig. 11.6.
Relatives: Simian Immunodeficiency Virus causes an AIDS-like disease in monkeys.

growths. Healthy people have over 800 helper T-cells in each mm^3 of blood, but in most HIV-infected people this number declines steadily over a period of some 10 years. The infections and cancers characteristic of AIDS set in when the helper T-cell count falls below about 200 per mm^3.

There is disagreement about precisely how HIV infection results in the disease AIDS. The standard theory is that the disease results directly from the steady loss of helper T-cells killed by HIV during the course of the infection, but this may be over-simple. Table 11.2 summarises the arguments for and against this and other suggested theories. It is quite likely that none of these proposed mecha-nisms is the *sole* cause of AIDS, but that the disease results from a combination of such effects.

No effective treatment for AIDS has so far been developed. The virus's complex replication cycle (see Fig. 11.6) offers many stages which could in theory be blocked by a suitable drug, but none has yet been found. HIV also has an unusually high mutation rate, making on average one or two changes to its genetic material in each replication cycle. This has made the development of anti-AIDS vaccines very difficult.

Q List *five* stages in HIV's replication cycle that might in principle be blocked by a suitable drug.

Q Why does HIV's high mutation rate hinder the development of anti-AIDS vaccines?

■ Prions and rare brain diseases

The disease of **scrapie** in sheep has been known since the 18th century and its infectious nature since the 1930s. Damage to brain cells results in sponge-like cavities. In the 1950s similar spongiform brains were observed in some tribes of Papua New Guinea where the disease **kuru** occurred in those who indulged in cannibalism. Sufferers became unsteady, lacked coordination and declined mentally and physically.

Another rare human disorder with similar symptoms is **Creutzfeld-Jakob disease (CJD)**. In the 1980s farmers started to observe in cattle a new disease which also had scrapie-like symptoms. It was named **Bovine spongiform encephalitis (BSE)** and the media, observing the staggering cattle, called it 'Mad cow disease'. Cattle feeds were made using offal from sheep and it was suggested that sheep suffering from scrapie may have in-fected the cattle.

Many scientists now believe that all of these spongiform brain diseases are caused, not by bacteria or viruses, but by **prions** (small proteinaceous infectious particles). Individual animals can inherit the ability to make prion particles and can also acquire them by infection. Some scientists do not believe that a single protein molecule can cause disease and assume that an information molecule (DNA or RNA) must be present though, as yet, it has not been detected.

Proposed mechanism	Evidence for theory	Drawbacks of theory
AIDS results from progressive destruction of helper T-cells by HIV	HIV does infect and destroy helper T-cells; heavy presence of HIV in lymph nodes ensures constant contact with T-cells passing through	No more than 1 in 500 T-cells are infected at any one time, but many more die
HIV destroys antigen presenting cells, preventing the 'priming' of T-cells in future infections	HIV does infect antigen presenting cells, and it has been shown that their ability to activate T-cells is then lost	Only a small proportion of antigen presenting cells appear to be infected
HIV's outer glycoprotein (gp-120 – see organism file) mimics MHC-II molecules, and 'tricks' the immune system into attacking itself	Computer models of the three-dimensional structure of HIV's gp-120 show similarity to human MHC-II	Foreign MHC-II alone does not cause AIDS: why should a substance that mimics it do so?

Table 11.2 Some theories linking HIV infection to AIDS

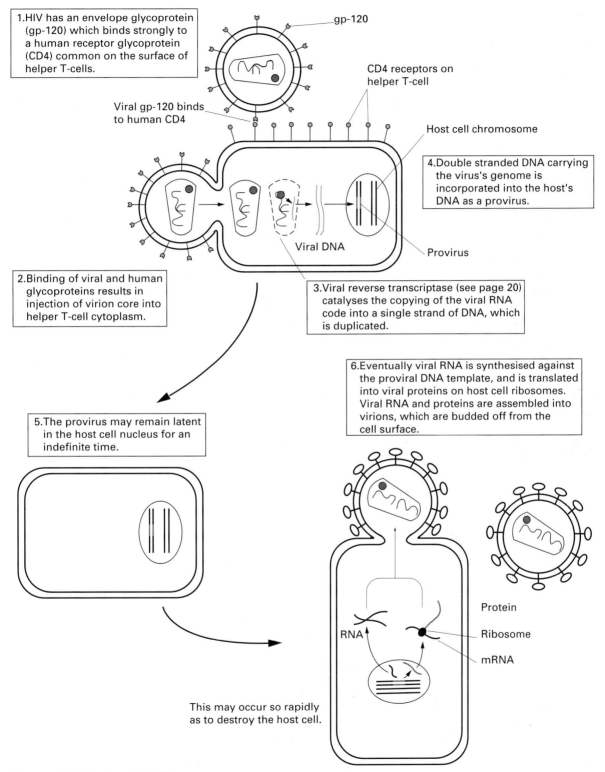

1. HIV has an envelope glycoprotein (gp-120) which binds strongly to a human receptor glycoprotein (CD4) common on the surface of helper T-cells.

gp-120

Viral gp-120 binds to human CD4

CD4 receptors on helper T-cell

Host cell chromosome

4. Double stranded DNA carrying the virus's genome is incorporated into the host's DNA as a provirus.

Viral DNA

Provirus

2. Binding of viral and human glycoproteins results in injection of virion core into helper T-cell cytoplasm.

3. Viral reverse transcriptase (see page 20) catalyses the copying of the viral RNA code into a single strand of DNA, which is duplicated.

6. Eventually viral RNA is synthesised against the proviral DNA template, and is translated into viral proteins on host cell ribosomes. Viral RNA and proteins are assembled into virions, which are budded off from the cell surface.

5. The provirus may remain latent in the host cell nucleus for an indefinite time.

Protein

RNA

Ribosome

mRNA

This may occur so rapidly as to destroy the host cell.

Figure 11.6 Cell infection cycle of HIV

■ Antibodies and their functioning

As stated earlier, antibodies are specialised protein molecules secreted by B-lymphocytes and involved in humoral immunity. The most striking characteristic of antibodies is their ability to bind strongly to the antigens that stimulate their secretion. The binding is achieved by the same kind of intermolecular forces that bind substrate molecules to the active sites of enzymes (see *Biology Advanced Studies – Biochemistry*), and like enzyme-substrate binding it is highly **specific**, that is, a particular antibody molecule will bind only to the antigen that its B-cell secretor detects, and to no other.

The effects of antibody-antigen binding vary according to the precise nature of both. Antibodies binding to antigens on the surface of invading microorganisms can cause the cells to *agglutinate* (that is, to stick together in clumps). This reduces the mobility of the pathogens, and also makes it easier for neutrophils to engulf them. Phagocytosis of pathogens is also aided by the fact that cells to which antibodies have bound adhere more readily to neutrophils: this is called *opsonic adherence*, and antibodies which have this effect are called *opsonins*.

Bound antibody is also a powerful activator of complement (see page 105). Among the components of complement activated by antibody-antigen complexes on the surface of cells are powerful *lytic enzymes*, which can literally digest holes in the surface of Gram-negative bacteria and other cells. Cells affected in this way may break up completely (*lysis*), or just 'leak to death'.

Antibodies against bacterial toxins are called *antitoxins*. By binding specifically to toxin molecules, they prevent them from exerting their toxic effects on human cells.

Chemically, antibodies form a distinct group of proteins, called **immunoglobulins**. There are five distinct classes of immunoglobulin: immunoglobulin G (abbreviated as IgG), IgM, IgA, IgD and IgE. Their properties are summarised in Table 11.3. IgG is the most abundant immunoglobulin in humans. Its molecular structure is shown in Figure 11.7.

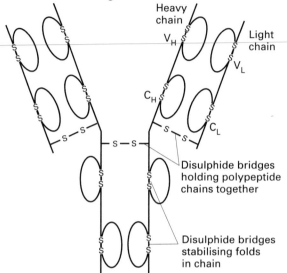

Figure 11.7 Molecular structure of an antibody G (IgG)

As you can see, an antibody molecule consists of four peptide chains, linked together by disulphide bridges in the shape of a Y. Two of the peptides are longer than the others, and are called heavy (H) chains; the others are the light (L) chains. Each chain in turn has a constant (C) region, whose amino acid sequence is identical in all the antibodies produced by an individual, and a variable (V) region which differs from one antibody to another. Each heavy chain thus has a V_H and a C_H region, and each light chain has a V_L and a C_L region.

It is the precise three-dimensional shape of the V regions of the four chains that gives each antibody its unique antigen-binding specificity, just as the precise three-dimensional shape of an enzyme's active site gives it its unique substrate-binding specificity. The three-dimensional folding of the C regions is important too: part of the C_H chain is responsible for complement activation, while the terminal C_H region binds the antibody-antigen complex to the surface of phagocytic cells (opsonic adherence).

The general features described above refer mainly to IgG, but apply broadly to all antibodies. Table 11.3 summarises the major distinguishing features of the five classes.

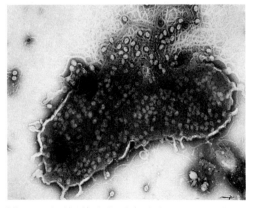

Micrograph showing lysis of a rod-shaped bacterium by T4 bacteriophages

Feature	IgG	IgA	IgM	IgD	IgE
Relative Molecular Mass (RMM)	150 000	160 000	9 000 000	185 000	200 000
Number of Y-shaped 4-peptide units	1	1	5	1	1
Number of antigen molecules bound	2	2	5 or 10	?	2
Percentage of total immunoglobulin	80	13	6	1	0.002
Other features	Abundant in tissue fluid. Crosses the placenta and is present in colostrum, giving immunity to newborn	Major immunoglobulin on mucous membranes: important in defence against microbial entry	Important in agglutination of microorganisms. Appears early in immune response	Present as receptor on lymphocyte surface, allowing lymphocyte to be activated by contact with antigen	Increases during parasitic infections. Responsible for symptoms of allergy

Table 11.3 Classes of immunoglobulin

■ Antibody synthesis and diversity

It is thought that any one individual can produce up to a million different structures (specificities), giving a very high probability that whatever the structure of an antigen, somewhere among the individual's lymphocytes there will be some that secrete an antibody to fit it. An important question to be asked, therefore, is how so many different protein structures (that is, so many different amino acid sequences) can be genetically encoded in one individual. An estimate for the total number of genes on all 23 pairs of human chromosomes is about 100 000 (though some give a number as high as one million), so it is almost certainly impossible to have one gene for every different antibody produced. This problem of 'Generation of Diversity' is one that has exercised immunologists for many years. Current thinking on the problem can be summarised as follows.

• Any one B-lymphocyte produces only one antibody structure. It carries this structure (as IgD) on its surface membrane, to act as a receptor for antigen binding.

• All B-lymphocytes carry a linked group of genes which code for the C regions and all possible V regions of both heavy and light antibody chains. During development each B-cell becomes 'committed' to reading only one V_L and one V_H gene, which combine with the genes encoding the C region to produce that cell's particular antibody.

• It has been suggested that the number of different V_H and V_L chains available might be increased by mutations in immature B-cells during their development.

• During the development of lymphocytes, any V_H/V_L combinations which happen to bind to self molecules are eliminated before they can mature.

■ Immunological memory

An important feature of the specific immune system is its memory. When a particular pathogen enters the body for the first time, it activates any T-cells and B-cells which happen to carry surface receptors fitting its antigens (in the case of T-cells, fitting fragments of its antigens attached to MHC molecules). These selected cells multiply repeatedly, producing a very large population of lymphocytes actively combating the infection. When the infection has been overcome, a large percentage of these lymphocytes persist as memory cells in the lymph nodes and elsewhere. If the same pathogen invades the body a second time, the memory cells are able to be activated very much more quickly and powerfully than on the first occasion (see Fig. 11.8).

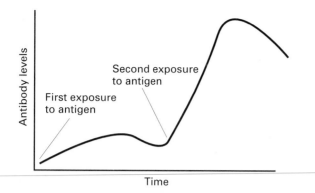

Antibody levels

First exposure to antigen

Second exposure to antigen

Time

Figure 11.8 Graph showing relative antibody production in first and second infection

It is because of the persistence of immunological memory that many diseases are caught only once: the common childhood diseases such as mumps, chickenpox and measles are good examples.

Q This does not apply to all diseases. Suggest why, despite the existence of immunological memory, some diseases (such as colds and 'flu) may be caught time after time.

■ **Vaccination**

The persistence of immunological memory is exploited in the process of vaccination against infectious disease. A vaccine is a solution or suspension containing antigens from a pathogen.

Depending on the vaccine, it may contain any of the following:

• **dead microbial cells or inactivated virions**. Because the organisms cannot multiply in the body, repeated injections of large doses may be necessary to stimulate a sufficient response from the immune system.

• **live organisms** of a weakened (*attenuated*) strain, incapable of causing disease but bearing antigens that stimulate a full immune response. Because these organisms can multiply in the body, only one small dose may be required. Active but attenuated viral vaccines also have the advantage that by infecting body cells they stimulate the multiplication of killer T-cells, some of which persist as memory cells. Dead viral vaccines cannot do this. There is, however, the risk that a weakened strain of a pathogen could mutate and become virulent again.

• **modified toxins** (*toxoids*). Toxins that are chemically altered by heat or chemical treatment: the modified molecules (toxoids) no longer have toxic effects on the host, but are similar enough to the original toxin molecules for antibodies made against them to be effective antitoxins.

• **pure chemical components** of the pathogen that are known to be antigenic. The development of genetic engineering techniques makes this the most likely form of future vaccine development.

Q What advantages are there in the use of purified antigenic components of pathogens as vaccines?

Nature of vaccine	Examples	Notes
Whole dead organisms	Salk polio vaccine Typhoid Whooping cough	This form of polio vaccine is injected. Very large dose needed, causing severe reaction. Cases of brain damage in vaccinated children caused concern. Likely to be replaced by a vaccine containing purified bacterial components.
Live attenuated organisms	Sabin polio vaccine	This form of polio vaccine is taken orally, often on a sugar lump.
Modified toxin (toxoid)	Tetanus Diphtheria	See the organism file on *Clostridium tetani*, page 92. Before the introduction of vaccination, diphtheria killed 2-3000 people (mostly young children) each year in the UK. It is now rare.
Purified antigen	Hepatitis B	A genetically engineered vaccine. A gene coding for a surface protein of the hepatitis B virus has been inserted into yeast cells, which produce the protein when grown in fermenters.

Table 11.4 Examples of vaccines of each type

Passive immunity

Immunity resulting from exposure to pathogens and subsequent production of antibodies and memory cells is called *active immunity*. This may be the result of an actual infection (*natural active immunity*) or of vaccination (*artificial active immunity*). However, temporary immunity can also be gained by receiving antibodies made outside the body: immunity gained in this way is called *passive immunity*. Passive immunity is gained in two main ways.

• Antibodies (specifically IgG - see page 113) pass across the placenta from mother to fetus, and are also present in colostrum (the first product of the breasts during lactation, thus a new-born baby's first food). In these ways a new-born baby gains some of its mother's acquired immunity.

• The use of *antisera* from vaccinated animals, from which antibodies may be extracted and purified. Antisera are usually used to give protection to people who have already been exposed to a pathogen. The process is called *passive immunisation*, and should not be confused with vaccination (which is *active immunisation*).

Q How do you think active and passive immunisation compare with respect to:
(a) the length of time it takes for the protection to become effective
(b) the length of time the protection lasts?
Explain your answer in each case.

Q Which form of immunisation would be most appropriate for the following?
(a) Someone who has cut herself on rusty barbed wire and may have been exposed to tetanus.
(b) A nurse who is leaving Britain next month to spend five years in an area where yellow fever is common.
Explain your answer in each case.

Genetic engineering techniques, and the development of monoclonal antibodies, are likely to mean that passive immunisation by injection of artificial 'tailor-made' antibodies will become increasingly common in the near future.

Chemotherapy

Chemotherapy is the use of drugs to combat disease. Drugs are chemicals from outside an organism's body which have a specific effect on its metabolism. Ideally, drugs used against infectious diseases need to interfere as much as possible with the pathogen's metabolism, and as little as possible with the host's metabolism. Early attempts to combat infectious disease with chemicals did not always recognise this simple rule. For example, in eighteenth century Europe the sexually transmitted disease syphilis was treated using mercury (II) chloride, a highly toxic substance which probably killed at least as many people as it cured.

The first widely effective antimicrobial drugs were the **sulphonamides**, discovered in 1935. They work by competing for the active site of a bacterial enzyme involved in the synthesis of folic acid, a growth factor. However, modern chemotherapy really dates from the discovery and purification of penicillin by Fleming, Chain and Florey between 1929 and 1940, and the subsequent development of this and other **antibiotics**.

Antibiotics may be defined as chemicals synthesised by microorganisms, which kill or suppress the growth of other microorganisms. (In practice, many of the antibiotics in current use are synthesised artificially, but all have been developed originally from microbial products.) Most are produced by fungi, or by *actinomycetes*, bacteria which grow in a filamentous, fungus-like way. They are active mainly against bacteria, generally by inhibiting or disrupting a specific step in bacterial metabolism. Some commonly used antibiotics are listed in Table 11.5.

Q Why should fungi have the metabolism to synthesise chemicals which specifically inhibit the growth of bacteria?

Q Most antibiotics act against bacteria, a few against fungi. Why are antibiotics more or less totally ineffective against viruses? And why, since this is so, are antibiotics often prescribed for people suffering from viral infections?

Drug resistance

When penicillin came into use during the Second World War, it was widely believed that bacterial disease would at last be eliminated as a cause of human suffering and death. The optimism proved ill-founded: by 1948, 75% of staphylococci isolated from patients and staff in hospitals were found to be penicillin-resistant, and the resistance spread quickly among other bacterial species. The pattern was repeated with later antibiotics such as tetracyclines and streptomycin: each was at first highly successful in curing a range of infections, but resistant strains of pathogens quickly arose and spread.

Antibiotic	Origin	Activity and uses
Penicillin	Moulds of the genus *Penicillium*, such as *P. chrysogenum*	Mimics a component of bacterial cell walls, so that bacteria exposed to penicillin build faulty walls and 'leak'. More effective against Gram-positive bacteria than Gram-negative ones. Many chemically similar derivatives: oxacillin, methicillin, cloxacillin, ampicillin, etc. Over-use in the past has led to widespread resistance among bacteria, and widespread allergy in patients.
Erythromycin	*Streptomyces erythreus*, a filamentous bacterium	Inhibits production of bacterial ribosomes. Effective against Gram-positive bacteria.
Nystatin	*Streptomyces noursei*	Useful against fungal infections such as thrush.
Tetracyclines	*Streptomyces* species	Interfere with protein synthesis. Effective against a range of Gram-positive and Gram-negative bacteria. Ineffective against fungi, and may encourage the growth of yeasts such as *Candida*: because of this, often given simultaneously with nystatin.
Streptomycin	*Streptomyces griseus*	Interferes with protein synthesis. Effective against Gram-positive and Gram-negative bacteria, and against *Mycobacterium tuberculosis* (see the case study on page 117).
Chloramphenicol	Originally from *Streptomyces venezuelae*, now synthesised artificially	Inhibits peptide bond synthesis in susceptible bacteria. Range of action similar to tetracyclines. Effective against *Salmonella*.

Table 11.5 Some important antibiotics

Drug resistance in microorganisms arises in the following way.
• Microorganisms occur in enormous numbers, and show great genetic variability. Like other organisms, their variation arises randomly, by mutation.
• When a newly developed antibiotic comes into use, almost all the pathogens against which it is used are susceptible to it – that is, they have a step in their metabolism which the antibiotic blocks or disrupts.
• Given such huge numbers and such great variability, it is likely that for virtually any step in any metabolic pathway, a large population of microorganisms will contain some individuals that carry out the step differently from the rest – perhaps by having a slightly different enzyme. These few individuals will be naturally resistant to the antibiotic.
• Extensive use of the new antibiotic wipes out the susceptible majority, but leaves the resistant minority unscathed. With their competitors wiped out, these few survivors multiply rapidly, passing on their resistance to their offspring to become the now-resistant majority (see Fig. 11.9). (This is, of course, a classic example of Darwinian evolution, with variation arising randomly through mutation, then spreading through the population by selection.) As if this were not bad enough, genes conferring drug resistance can be passed from one bacterial species to another on plasmids exchanged during conjugation. In this way, resistance first arising in a non-pathogenic species can quickly be passed on to a pathogenic one – for example, from *Escherichia coli* to gut pathogens such as *Salmonella* or *Shigella*.

Q It is widely agreed that the spread among bacteria of resistance to antibiotics such as penicillin was greatly accelerated by their over-use, especially early on. Explain the reasoning behind this claim.

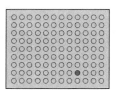  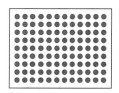

1. In a large enough population of microorganisms a small number are naturally resistant through random genetic variation.

2. Exposure to antibiotic eliminates the susceptible majority

3. The small number of resistant survivors multiply rapidly in the absence of competition.

4. The population is now more or less 100% antibiotic-resistant.

Figure 11.9 Evolution of antibiotic resistance in bacteria

DRUG RESISTANCE: THE CASE OF TUBERCULOSIS

Tuberculosis ('TB') is caused by an aerobic rod-shaped bacterium called *Mycobacterium tuberculosis*. The organism infects one in three of the entire world population; it can live and multiply in most human organs, though in Europe it is most commonly associated with the lungs. It produces no toxins, causing disease by its invasiveness and its interactions with host tissues. These include stimulating the formation of the hard, round nodules called *tubercles* which give the disease its name. Infection is most commonly by inhaled droplets, but other routes of entry are possible – for example, by drinking milk from cattle infected with bovine tuberculosis.

Within the body, the bacteria spread to all organs by way of the blood and lymphatic systems. Once established in a tissue, they live mainly inside body cells. This protects them from both antibodies and drugs, and enables them to persist in the body for years or even decades.

A number of drugs have been found to be effective in treating TB, if taken for a long enough period. The main ones are as follows:
• **streptomycin** (see Table 11.5)
• **isoniazid**, for many years the drug of first choice
• **PAS** (para-aminosalicylic acid) – less potent that isoniazid or streptomycin, but used with them to hinder the emergence of isoniazid-resistant or streptomycin-resistant varieties
• **rifampicin**, an antibiotic that interferes with mRNA synthesis.

As a result of the selection process summarised in Fig. 11.10, TB bacteria resistant to one or another of these drugs arise quite easily. Because of this, conventional medical practice has been to treat patients with a combination of most or all of the drugs, on the grounds that any bacteria in the patient's body which are resistant to, for example, isoniazid are likely to be killed by rifampicin, and *vice versa*. The chances of random mutations in a bacterial cell simultaneously creating resistance to several drugs at once are very remote indeed.

However, this strategy has been foiled by two major problems.
• Doctors inexperienced in TB tratment have tended to prescribe too few drugs.
• Patients taking anti-TB drugs tend to give them up when they feel better, rather than continuing until they are completely free of infection (which may take up to two years).

The result of these failings has been to allow large populations of bacteria to develop which are resistant to one or another drug. If these large populations are then exposed to a second drug, there is a good chance that somewhere among them there will be a few individuals resistant to that one too. (The chance of any *one* rifampicin-resistant bacterium also being resistant to isoniazid is very remote; but among, say, 10^{10} rifampicin-resistant bacteria, the chance of there being one or two that also happen to be isoniazid-resistant is quite high.) In this way, so-called **multi-drug resistant** (MDR) strains of tuberculosis bacteria have been selected. In Britain, only about 2% of reported TB cases involve drug-resistant strains. In New York, however, about 20% of strains are resistant to both isoniazid and rifampicin, and some do not respond to any of the known anti-TB drugs.

So far, many of those who have died of multi-drug resistant tuberculosis have also been HIV-positive, making it difficult to estimate how much of a threat MDR strains pose to the population as a whole. They can hardly, however, be good news.

Patterns of disease

We take it for granted that some diseases are always with us, as part of our everyday lives. In Britain, the common cold is the classic example: when was the last day when *no-one* in your school or college had a cold? These 'ever-present' diseases are said to be **endemic** in a community.

We also take for granted the fact that many diseases come and go, or rise and fall in their incidence. Measles and 'flu are good examples, and so are some types of food poisoning. We call the sudden appearance of a disease in a community, or a sudden rise in the number of people who have it, an **epidemic**. If an epidemic is so widespread as to cover many countries, it is called a **pandemic**.

But why is it that some diseases are always present in the community? Why those particular diseases, and not others? And why, after being rare or unknown for many years, should diseases suddenly flare up in epidemics?

A disease can be endemic in a community only if two conditions are met.

• The population is large enough to sustain the necessary *chain of infection* from one host to another. In very small populations, such a large proportion of the community may become immune to the disease (or may be killed by it) that too few susceptible hosts are left for the pathogen to be passed on, and the disease dies out.

• Social conditions in the community offer no effective barrier to its spread. Cholera and typhoid are endemic in parts of Asia and Africa because inadequate sanitation allows faecal contamination of drinking water. Neither is endemic in Europe, as sewage is effectively treated and drinking water is purified (see Chapter 8). Our endemic diseases are mostly contagious or droplet infections whose spread cannot be effectively controlled by hygiene, sanitation or vaccination. Colds, for example, are caused by several hundred varieties of small RNA viruses (rhinoviruses). Vaccination against any one of them gives no protection against the others, and is therefore useless as a control measure. As colds are spread by contact and by sneezed-out droplets, and as it is impossible to isolate all people with colds from contact with others, they are endemic.

Epidemics of disease usually break out in one of three ways.

• By the introduction of a pathogen into a community which has had no previous contact with it. During the colonial expansions of the seventeenth, eighteenth and nineteenth centuries, Europeans carried many of their endemic diseases to the native peoples of America, Africa and Asia, and the subsequent epidemics caused appalling mortality among native populations. In New Zealand the Maori population fell from an estimated 180 000 at the beginning of the nineteenth century to about 40 000 at the end, largely due to measles and syphilis introduced by Europeans.

• By the appearance of a new or more virulent form of a pathogen through mutation. The influenza (flu) virus (especially the variety known as Type A) is notorious for its regular mutation rate, giving a major new flu epidemic roughly every ten years. Because the virus's coat protein is altered by the mutation, immunity acquired from previous flu infections has no effect on the new form, which spreads unhindered through the population. The most recent pandemic was caused by the A-Beijing flu virus in the winter of 1991-2, but on this occasion the disease failed to reach epidemic proportions in the UK. In the most distant past, the flu pandemic of 1919 killed some 20 000 000 people worldwide, considerably more than the four years of world war which preceded it. (See the organism file on page 120 for more details of the flu virus.)

• By a major upheaval in social conditions, allowing the spread of a pathogen which previous custom or technology had excluded or had confined to a very low level. At its most drastic, the upheaval may be a natural catastrophe such as a flood or an earthquake. Such events are commonly followed by epidemics of water-borne infections like typhoid or cholera, which the community's sanitation system had previously excluded, but which spread freely when broken sewers overflow into drinking water. Less dramatically, a change in social habits or custom can affect the occurrence of a disease. The relaxation in attitudes to sexual behaviour during the 1960s, and the simultaneous arrival of the contraceptive pill (a reliable contraceptive, but one offering no defence against infection), were followed in the 1970s by a marked rise in the incidence of gonorrhoea and other sexually transmitted diseases – enough, in the case of gonorrhoea, to constitute at least a minor epidemic.

The most widely publicised epidemic of recent years has, of course, been AIDS (see page 110). It is likely that all three of the above causes have operated in this case.

• HIV was introduced to new populations of hosts across the world, probably from Africa and probably as long ago as the 1960s.

• HIV itself may be the product of a mutation in a virus such as Simian Immunodeficiency Virus (which infects monkeys), allowing it to jump the species barrier and infect humans. People in some African countries with tropical rainforest do eat monkey meat, so those who come into close contact with raw, bloody, infected monkey flesh or meat could, unwittingly, risk such infection. HIV's own very high mutation rate is also a factor in defeating its hosts' immune systems.

• The spread of HIV in Western countries was undoubtedly helped by changes in sexual attitudes and behaviour, such as greater acceptance of, and openness about, male homosexuality.

By definition, an epidemic does not last for ever. In theory, there are two possible outcomes to an epidemic.

• The chain of infection is broken completely, either because the pathogen runs out of susceptible hosts or because temporarily disrupted barriers are restored. Either way, the disease disappears from the community. This seems to have happened to the plague epidemics of 1348 and 1665: presumably, after massive mortality too few susceptible people were left to keep the chain of infection going. In modern times, vaccination and chemotherapy may be used to reduce the pool of susceptible hosts.

• By the operation of natural selection, the pathogen becomes less virulent and the host more resistant, until eventually the two populations live in equilibrium, the disease now being endemic. This is illustrated diagrammatically in Fig. 11.10.

Q The process shown in Fig. 11.10 has probably occurred many times in history, giving us our familiar (but still occasionally fatal) endemic diseases such as flu and measles. There is much debate about whether it will happen in the case of AIDS. State the arguments for and against.

1. First contact between pathogen and community

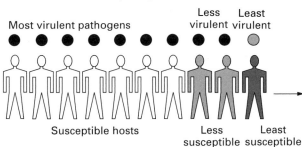

2. After a few generations

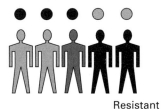

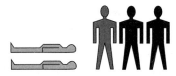

3. After sufficient generations

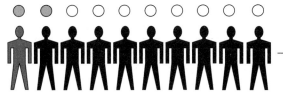

Most of human population is now resistant

Figure 11.10 Transition from epidemic to endemic disease

ORGAMISM FILE: Influenza virus

Description: RNA virus of the *myxovirus* group. Capsid roughly spherical, 70 nm in diameter, with a lipid envelope about 110 nm in diameter. Occurs in three immunologically distinct varieties, influenza types A, B and C: each of these is subdivided into numerous distinct strains.

Habitat: respiratory mucosa of humans and other mammals.

Importance: inductive agent of influenza (flu). Influenza is endemic at low levels in most communities, and is characterised by regular large-scale epidemics, often reaching pandemic proportions. Only influenza type A causes serious epidemics, resulting from mutations bringing about changes in its surface antigens. The major surface antigens are a *haemagglutinin* protein, important in binding the virions to the cells they infect, and an enzyme called *neuraminidase* which helps the virus to penetrate cell membranes.

Influenza is caught by droplet infection. Virions enter and replicate within cells lining the respiratory tract. After 4–8 hours, a single infected cell yields about 60–120 new virions. These are released from the intact cell rather than by lysis, and go on to infect new cells. Symptoms appear one or two days after infection, and include chills, fever, fatigue, headaches and muscular pain. The upper respiratory tract becomes inflamed, leading to nasal discharge and sneezing. There is no

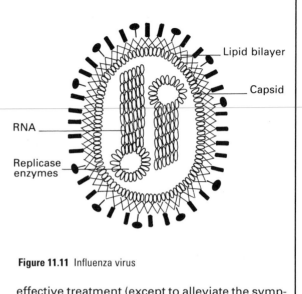

Figure 11.11 Influenza virus

effective treatment (except to alleviate the symptoms), and after three or four days of fever recovery is rapid unless complications have set in. The commonest complication is pneumonia, which can be fatal in the elderly or in young children.

Relatives: the influenza group of the myxoviruses includes viruses causing swine flu, horse flu, duck flu and fowl plague. Other groups of myxoviruses include those causing canine distemper, as well as the mumps/measles group (see page 96).

■ MICROBIAL DISEASES OF PLANTS

Infectious plant diseases are mostly fungal or viral in origin, only rarely bacterial. For convenience, plant diseases can be regarded as occurring in three phases: the **pre-penetration phase**, involving the dispersal of the pathogen to a new host and its initial growth or germination on the host's surface; the **penetration phase**, covering the actual entry into the plant; and the **post-penetration phase**, which involves the growth of the pathogen inside the plant, its feeding on or from the plant's tissues, its reproduction and the release of its own offspring to be dispersed in their turn.

■ The pre-penetration phase

As plants are not motile, plant pathogens need to have reliable modes of transmission from one plant or plant population to another. Some examples are shown in Table 11.6.

As you can see, fungi have a number of specialised means of spreading themselves, such as the production of huge numbers of airborne spores. Most plant viruses have also evolved specialised transmission methods, most commonly insect vectors such as aphids. Some plant viruses multiply in their insect vector as well as in their plant host. By comparison, the spread of bacterial pathogens of plants is much more haphazard.

Means of transmission	Examples
Direct growth from one host to another	Some soil fungi, e.g. *Armillaria mellea*, the honey fungus, a parasite of trees; some viruses are also transmitted by such fungi.
Airborne spores	Most fungi infecting aerial parts of plants.
Raindrops and water splashes	Some bacteria and fungal spores.
Animal vectors	Most plant viruses, the commonest vectors being insects such as aphids and leafhoppers, with piercing and sucking mouthparts; soil nematodes spread some root-infecting viruses.
Seed-borne infections	Some fungi spread from generation to generation in or on seeds: examples include wheat smut, and the fungi causing 'damping-off' of seedlings; lettuce mosaic virus is seed-borne, others are transmitted in bulbs or tubers; barley false stripe virus is transmitted in pollen grains.

Table 11.6 The transmission of diseases from plant to plant

■ The penetration phase

There are four ways in which plant pathogens gain entry to their hosts:
• through natural openings such as stomata and lenticels (bacteria and some fungi)
• through wounds or damaged epidermal cells (bacteria, some fungi, some viruses)
• by growing through the intact cuticle (certain specialised fungi)
• direct injection by an animal vector (most viruses).

Bacteria, as we see, are entirely dependent on being carried in through some natural or accidental opening in the plant surface. Some viruses, too, are known to be transmitted through abrasions, when, for example, the leaves of infected plants are blown against those of non-infected plants. Only some specialised fungi can penetrate plants through the intact cuticle, a feat they achieve using a specialised hypha with a swollen tip called an **appressorium**.

As the name suggests, the appressorium is pressed hard against the plant surface, and apparently by pressure alone forces one or more fine penetration hyphae (infection pegs) through the cuticle into the underlying tissue (see Fig. 11.12).

■ The post-penetration phase

There are two contrasting ways in which plant pathogens go about exploiting the host's tissues and resources. **Necrotrophic** pathogens do so in a destructive way, causing rapid death and degradation of host tissues as they spread through them, and usually quickly killing the whole plant. Many necrotrophs are then able to continue feeding saprophytically on the host's dead remains. **Biotrophic** pathogens establish a more stable relationship with the host, penetrating and feeding on host cells without causing the widespread death and destruction characteristic of necrotrophs. Biotrophs are more specialised parasites, often restricted to one or a few host species and in many cases incapable of growing anywhere other than their host's living tissues. (This makes some biotrophic pathogens difficult to study, as they cannot be grown on artificial media in the laboratory.) Some features of necrotrophic and biotrophic plant pathogens are compared in Table 11.7.

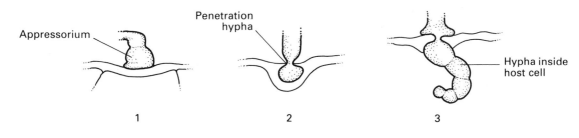

Figure 11.12 Appressorium of *Botrytis*

121

Feature	Necrotrophic pathogens	Biotrophic pathogens
Host range	Usually wide, non-specific; some can infect only damaged or weakened plants, entering through wounds	Usually restricted to one or a few specific hosts; entry by way of natural openings
Feeding strategy	Use powerful degrading enzymes such as pectinases and cellulases to break down host tissues; breakdown products then absorbed	Specialised feeding structures such as **haustoria** (Fig. 11.14) which penetrate host cells and extract nutrients
Toxin production	Often produced	None
Examples	Bacteria such as *Erwinia*, causing soft rots Fungi such as *Fusarium*, causing vascular wilts, and *Phytophthora infestans*, causing potato blight	Bacteria such as *Agrobacterium tumefaciens*, causing crown gall in fruit trees and beet Fungi such as *Puccinia*, causing rusts, and *Erysiphe*, causing powdery mildews

Table 11.7 Comparison of necrotrophic and biotrophic pathogens

Biotrophic pathogens are sufficiently well adapted to their hosts to avoid triggering the usual plant responses to parasitic attack (see below). This is probably one of the factors that restricts their host range, as the precise biochemical 'fine tuning' that allows a biotroph to coexist with a plant without setting off its alarm system is unlikely to work in different host species. Necrotrophs, on the other hand, simply overwhelm the host plant's defences with their destructive enzymes and, often, toxins. The soil fungus *Fusarium* produces toxins which are carried upwards in the host's xylem vessels and cause wilting. *Pseudomonas tabaci*, a bacterium which causes tobacco wildfire disease, produces a toxin that interferes with its host's amino acid metabolism. In these and other cases, the toxin kills host cells either locally or throughout the plant, thus preventing it from mounting a defensive response to the pathogen, and enabling the pathogen to spread more easily into the dead or dying tissues.

More detailed treatments of the post-penetration phase of an important necrotrophic disease and of an important biotrophic one are given in the organism files on page 123.

■ **Specific effects on plant growth**

Although biotrophic infections do not (at least immediately) kill the host plant, they may have a considerable effect on its growth. The pathogen may simply reduce its host's photosynthesis rate, or divert the products of photosynthesis from the host's tissues to its own: either way, the effect is to retard the host plant's growth (and, in the case of crop plants, to reduce yield). However, some pathogens have much more specific effects on plant growth, often associated with microbial products similar or identical to the plant's own growth substances ('plant hormones'). *Taphrina cerasi* is a fungal pathogen of cherry trees. It produces a substance which causes normally dormant buds to develop, giving rise to a growth known as 'witch's broom'. The bacterium *Agrobacterium tumefaciens* causes localised growths called crown galls in fruit trees and sugar beet. It has been shown to produce indole-acetic acid (IAA), one of the family of plant growth substances called auxins, but this particular pathogen also affects its host's growth genetically, by inserting a plasmid (the T_i plasmid) into the chromosome of infected cells which triggers them to divide.

Q Why has this made *Agrobacterium tumefaciens* a favourite tool for researchers seeking to improve crop plants by genetic engineering?

ORGANISM FILE: *Fusarium* species

Description: deuteromycete fungi consisting of haploid mycelium bearing multicellular asexual spores (macroconidia). These are often borne on tufts of tangled hyphae. In unfavourable conditions the mycelium breaks up into thick-walled resistant spores (chlamydospores). The genus is large and variable, and identification of individual species can be difficult.

Habitat: soil; opportunistic necrotrophic pathogens of numerous plant species.

Importance: inductive agents of vascular wilts of a wide range of higher plants, including many that are commercially important.

Infection occurs from mycelium or spores in the soil, often entering through wounds. The hyphae produce cellulose-digesting enzymes which enable *Fusarium* to invade and break down host tissues. The wilting characteristic of infected plants is caused by physical blockage of xylem vessels, preventing the upward transport of water from the roots to the shoot, and also by toxins such as fusaric acid produced by the fungus. When the host plant has died, *Fusarium* continues to live saprophytically on its remains.

Relatives: Volutell fructi, inductive agent of dry rot of apples.

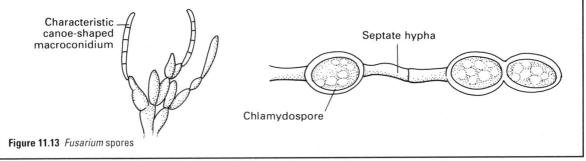

Figure 11.13 *Fusarium* spores

ORGANISM FILE: *Erysiphe graminis*

Description: ascomycete fungus; obligate parasite.

Habitat: surface of cereals and other grasses.

Importance: inductive agent of powdery mildew of cereals, an important biotrophic infection. The fungus grows as a dense mycelium on the surface of leaves, penetrating epidermal cells with haustoria to obtain food. The mycelium greatly reduces the amount of light reaching the leaf surface, thus reducing photosynthesis and growth. The characteristic powdery appearance results from the formation of millions of asexual spores (conidia) borne in chains on the end of aerial hyphae (conidiophores).

Conidia are released into the air to infect other hosts. Unlike other powdery mildews, *Erysiphe graminis* does not reproduce sexually.

Relatives: The powdery mildews form an important family of plant pathogens, infecting many commercial crops. They include the following:

Fungus	Host plant(s)
Sphaerotheca mors-uvae	Gooseberry
Podosphaera leucotricha	Apple
Sphaerotheca humuli	Hop, strawberry
Uncinula necator	Vine
Oidium chrysanthemi	Chrysanthemum

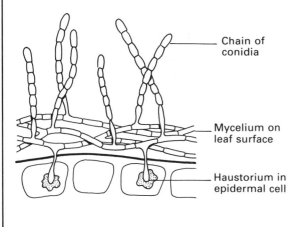

Figure 11.14 *Erysiphe graminis* showing the specialised feeding structures called haustoria

123

Viral diseases of plants

Since the terms biotrophic and necrotrophic refer to feeding strategies, they cannot properly be applied to plant viral diseases, as viruses do not 'feed' in the usual sense of the term. As a general rule, however, the course of a viral disease in a plant is more similar to a biotrophic infection than a necrotrophic one: the host may not be killed, at least not immediately, and cases of long-term coexistence between virus and host plant are common. In fact, some commercially important decorative plants rely on resident viruses for their patterning: examples include 'broken' (striped) tulip flowers, and the attractively mottled leaves of the houseplant *Abutilon* – both patterns are caused by viruses.

Plant viruses are all RNA viruses, and appear to infect Angiosperms (flowering plants) only, never gymnosperms, ferns or lower plants. Experimentally, most plant viruses are found to be capable of infecting a range of hosts, but in nature each tends to be restricted (perhaps by competition or by lack of suitable vectors) to one or a few. The infections they cause may be systemic (the virus spreading throughout the entire plant) or localised. The same virus can cause systemic infection in one host and only localised lesions in another: for example, tobacco mosaic virus is systemic in tobacco, but causes only local spots on the leaves of related plants. Systemic infections are likely to stunt growth and reduce crop yields. Other common symptoms include spotting or mottling of leaves, leaf curl, and sometimes wilitng and premature leaf fall. As with some fungi and bacteria, there may be abnormal growth patterns, such as 'witches' brooms' caused by growth of normally dormant lateral buds, or the wart-like growths on cucumber fruits caused by cucumber mosaic virus.

Unlike animal viruses, which usually exist as naked nucleic acid in host cells and wear their protein coats only when released, plant viruses are found as fully coated virions inside the cells of their plant host. This is probably related to transmission: an aphid or other vector feeding on the plant will take up whole virions, which are better able to survive passage in or on the vector than could naked RNA.

The organism file opposite gives more detail of potato leaf roll virus, an important pest of potato crops.

ORGANISM FILE: Potato leaf roll virus

Description: RNA virus; roughly spherical protein coat containing single RNA strand.
Habitat: tissues of potato and related plants.
Importance: inductive agent of leaf roll of potato. Presence of the virus causes the host to store the products of photosynthesis in its leaves (largely as starch) instead of translocating them to growth and storage areas: as a result infected plants are stunted, with small, curled leaves and a greatly reduced crop of tubers (the parts of the potato plant that we eat).

Transmission is by aphids, and from generation to generation through infected tubers. In the UK, commercial stocks of 'seed' potatoes (small tubers used for planting) are kept free from leaf roll virus by rearing them in the colder climate of Scotland and Northern Ireland, where the aphids carrying the viruses cannot overwinter and where they do not arrive until after the seed potato crop has been lifted.

Plant defences

Plants defend themselves against infectious disease by means of structural barriers to microbial entry and/or spread, and also by means of chemical inhibitors of microbial growth. Some of these defence mechanisms are present independently of microbial attack, as part of the normal structure and composition of the plant, whilst others are induced specifically by invading microorganisms. Table 11.8 summarises some of the main components of the defensive systems of plants.

Control of plant diseases

Controlling infectious diseases of plants can be approached in a variety of ways, including the following.
• **General plant hygiene.** This includes avoiding overcrowding, removal of diseased individuals or parts (including the remains of harvested plants), and removal of wild plants that might act as a reservoir for pathogens. On a small scale, sterilisation of soil (for example by fumigation) can

'Inbuilt' structural barriers	Cuticle	Thicker cuticles are less easily penetrated: plums with thicker cuticles are shown to be more resistant to brown rot (the fungus *Sclerotinia*) than others. Cuticles may also be impregnated with toxic chemicals.
	Stomata	Citrus fruits with tight-closing guard cells are resistant to the bacterium *Pseudomonas citri*, those with more open stomata are not.
	Bark	Tough, dry, lignified, and impregnated with tannins (see below).
	Cork	Made of suberin, difficult to penetrate and break down.
Barriers produced as response to wounds or infection	Gums and resins	Secreted from cells at the site of a wound, harden and block entry of pathogens. Gums and resins may also be secreted as plugs into xylem or phloem to block movement of pathogens inside plant.
	Tyloses	A tylosis is a balloon-like extension into a xylem vessel of a neighbouring thin-walled cell. Several tyloses can block the vessel, restricting spread of pathogens (see Fig. 11.15).
	Cork barriers	Active formation of a cork layer over a wound restricts entry. Seen in corky scab of potato (the fungus *Spongospora solani*).
Chemical defences	Tannins and phenols	The resistance of bark and wood to fungal invasion is linked to their tannin content.
	Acids	The high acid content of citrus fruits (mostly citric acid) makes them less liable to infection by both bacterial and fungal pathogens.
	Mustard oil	Important in crucifers such as cabbage.
	Phytoalexins	Produced by damaged cells in the vicinity of microbial invasion, able in tiny concentrations to inhibit microbial growth: mainly anti-fungal and anti-viral, no effect on viruses. Specific to the plant species producing them, not to the microorganisms on which they act.
	Pathogenesis-related (PR) proteins	Produced in response to infection, by healthy as well as infected tissues – suggesting chemical communication between healthy and infected tissues. Over twenty identified in tobacco, including *chitinase*, which may work by breaking down fungal cell walls.

Table 11.8 Plant defences

eliminate resting stages such as bacterial or fungal spores.

• Planting **disease-free stock**. This includes, for example, using 'seed' potatoes from colder regions such as Scotland, as these avoid infection with viruses such as potato leaf roll (see the organism file on page 124).

• **Vector control**. The most important vectors of plant diseases are insects such as aphids. Protection may be given by contact insecticides such as malathion or by systemic insecticides such as thiofanox, but the enormous size of aphid populations make the evolution of resistance highly likely: insecticides also have the drawback of reducing populations of beneficial insects. Alternative approaches include research into biological control, and removing plants on which aphids overwinter from the vicinity of susceptible crops.

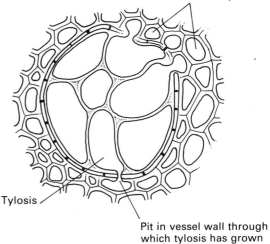

Parenchyma cells

Tylosis

Pit in vessel wall through which tylosis has grown

Figure 11.15 Tyloses in a xylem vessel

• **Control of cultural conditons**. Careful control of soil conditions such as moisture content, pH and mineral content can limit a crop's liability to attack by pathogens. For example, over-watering encourages invasion of plants by *Botrytis cinerea*, a necrotrophic fungus, whilst excessively dry soil encourages powdery mildews.

• **Chemical control**. Fungal diseases may be controlled by contact or systemic fungicides. Contact (or surface) fungicides remain on the surface of the plant and either prevent the germination of fungal spores, or kill the fungus immediately after germination: either way, infection is prevented. In the past, Bordeaux mixture and lime-sulphur were important contact fungicides. Bordeaux mixture consists of copper sulphate and calcium hydroxide. The mixture releases copper ions on contact with water, and these kill the fungus. Lime-sulphur is a mixture of sulphur and calcium hydroxide, which slowly releases toxic hydrogen sulphide on the plant surface. It is still used to control powdery mildew on grapes. Modern contact fungicides include dithiocarbamate compounds such as Maneb and Mancozeb, used to control potato blight. All contact fungicides need to be applied before fungal infection occurs, and they may be washed off by rain: the timing of their application is therefore crucial. Repeated applications are needed during the growing season. Contact fungicides are also commonly used as dressings on the outside of seeds, protecting them from soil fungi before germination.

Systemic fungicides are taken up by the plant and are present throughout its structure: they can thus kill fungal pathogens after they have invaded, as well as protecting against future infection. They include Benomyl, and triadimefon (sold as Bayleton), which interferes with sterol synthesis in fungi. At present, only about 20% of fungicides used worldwide are systemic, but their importance is growing.

• **Biological control**. Some soil-borne plant diseases, such as potato scab (caused by the bacterium *Streptomyces scabies*), can be partially controlled by using compost to encourage the growth of competitive soil saprophytes. More specifically, frost damage to strawberry plants has been found to be encouraged by a form of the bacterium *Pseudomonas syringae*, the cells of which act as centres for ice crystal formation. The form of *Pseudomonas syringae* which does this is called ice$^+$. Spraying strawberry crops with a different form of the bacterium (ice$^-$) reduces the ice$^+$ population by competiton, and thus reduces frost damage.

• **Breeding resistant varieties**. It is commonly found that the wild ancestors of crop plants are resistant to diseases to which the crops are susceptible. The mechanism of resistance is usually under genetic control, and conventional cross-breeding, often over many generations, can sometimes lead to the incorporation of the 'resistance' gene or genes into the crop whilst at the same time retaining the crop's superior yield. In cases where the crop plant is too genetically different from its wild relative to be crossed conventionally, biotechnological techniques such as genetic engineering or protoplast fusion may be used.

For the genetic engineering of resistant plants, the T_i plasmid of the crown gall bacterium, *Agrobacterium tumefaciens*, is a popular vector for the transfer of resistance genes. The plasmid's own tumour-inducing genes are removed, and the desired resistance-related genes spliced into it using conventional genetic engineering techniques (see page 79). The transformed bacteria are allowed to infect the host plant, usually in tissue culture, thus inserting the resistance-related genes into their chromosomes. This technique has been successful with a number of broad-leaved plants, but less so with cereals, which *Agrobacterium tumefaciens* does not readily infect.

The technique of protoplast fusion (see page 72) has been successfully used to produce somatic hybrids between domesticated potatoes (*Solanum tuberosum*) and a reproductively incompatible wild species (*Solanum brevidens*) which is resistant to several important potato viruses.

BIOTECHNOLOGY AND THE FUTURE

In the same week that the world's press was announcing the horrors of outbreaks of bubonic plague and pneumonic plague in India (see the newspaper extract on page 128), the American Health Secretary was telling the world that the disease of polio had been wiped out in the US – there had been no cases for over three years; the British government was warning that measles was about to break out and that all school children were to be vaccinated; and yet another research team was announcing yet another *possible* cancer cure. Today, research reports in medical biotechnology, agriculture and the food industry reel out from the presses faster than anyone can file them – let alone read them! The subjects are developing at a frenetic rate. It has become almost impossible for the scientists working in microbiology and biotechnology to keep up to date in any but their own narrow areas of research.

So what hope is there for the layperson to understand the advances in this branch of science? We believe that all scientists have a duty to help in the public understanding of science. At the same time the media should have a responsibility to report science accurately so as to avoid raising false hopes, and to refuse to publish foolish scare stories. Biologists must be ready to answer a number of questions.

■ Does the public know enough to make decisions?

In 1993 a report of a committee set up by the UK government made recommendations about the use of genetically modified organisms as food. They said that the aim should be 'to make practical provision for **informed choice by consumers** in accordance with their individual ethical insights'. Think about the issue. In the research to produce transgenic sheep (see page 82) most of the lambs born did not have the required gene. The question was: can they be used for human food? And, if the successful transgenic sheep were not so valuable, could their meat have been used?

The committee chaired by a priest with science qualifications came to the conclusion that 'there is no overriding ethical objection which requires absolute prohibition of food containing copy genes of human origin'. However they accepted that some religious or vegetarian groups might have dietary or ethical objects so 'the food should be labelled and information should be made available by industry and government'. You may like to consider the following.
• Is PCR copying of human genes the same as using human material?
• Is it 'unnatural' or 'interfering with nature' to make transgenics?
• Should vegetarians accept transgenes (e.g. rennin)?

■ Is it right to patent the sequences of DNA?

There has been furious debate about whether scientists discovering things about living organisms should be able to patent their discoveries. It may be a valid debating point to say that they did not invent the DNA sequence so they have no rights over it. On the other hand, the huge multi-national companies researching medicine and food crops would be unlikely to invest in very expensive research unless they were certain of a suitable financial return. There is a strong argument that once a discovery has been patented there is no longer a need for commercial secrecy and the information can be more widely disseminated. There is a subtle difference between discoveries (which may not be patented) and techniques and procedures (which may). In 1980 a scientist in the USA, Ananda Chakrabarty, gained the first patent on a genetically engineered *Pseudomonas* bacterium that could be used to clear up oil spills. The court decided that the new strain was 'the result of human ingenuity and research'. Do you think that:
• the host organism and the recombinant gene already existed?
• Chakrabarty was right to protect it with a patent?
• DNA is a sequence of letters and suitable for copyright laws?

127

■ What about animal welfare considerations?

The OncoMouse (page 83) was engineered to have a human gene that caused it to develop cancer and die. Milk production in cattle can be increased by up to 30% by injections of growth hormone (BST). There is some evidence that a small number of cattle may suffer. There is also a suggestion that bigger herds will result and smaller farms will go out of business.

• Do scientists have a right to manipulate animals?
• Is the OncoMouse study justified if it results in a cancer cure?
• What are the advantages and disadvantages of using BST?

There is talk of developing transgenic pigs that could be used to grow organs (such as heart valves) suitable for transplanting into humans.

• Are there really any differences in conducting research on mammals rather than other organisms – like yeasts, *E. coli*, tomato plants or viruses?

■ How much do you want to know about *your* DNA?

It could be possible to work out a gene profile for each of us. In some cases it could be important to know that we are carriers of certain recessive genes – after all, one in twenty of us carries a cystic fibrosis allele. We could be screened to see which genetic diseases we may develop as we get older. Would you want to know? Might your employer want to know? And what about your insurance company?

■ What are the dangers of releasing genetically modified organisms (GMOs) into the environment?

There may be some danger in releasing such organisms which could compete with the native species. Laboratory microbes could have an adverse effect on ecosystems, but regulations already exist which limit such risks. The important thing is that scientists should keep everyone fully informed about any potential release and that regulations should exist to monitor the outcome and to ensure the proper clean up at the end of a trial or at other times if it should be necessary.

Apocalypse now?

The magnitude 6.6 earthquake that ravaged parts of Maharashtra in India late last year continues to claim lives. In its wake has come an old enemy: bubonic plague. According to the Indian National Institute of Communicable Diseases, which has a team in the area, the number of suspected plague deaths has risen to 64. Most of them are around the town of Latur, in the area where 10,000 people died. Bodies were buried or burned hastily and survivors moved into safer shelters. The older houses – at least those still standing – were, according to newspaper reports, used as granaries.

Then the rats moved in. Bubonic plague, notoriously, is transmitted by fleas from rats to humans. Health authorities have sprayed the area with DDT, and the health ministry has been claiming that the outbreak is under control.

But the pool of old killers – cholera, dysentery, diphtheria, tuberculosis, plague – is out there, waiting to seize the moment, and natural disasters have a way of providing the moment.

Yersinia pestis – the bacterium responsible for bubonic plague, and transmitted by fleas living along with communities of rats - turned up in Europe in 1347 and in four years killed one third of the population. It kept popping up, at intervals, for the rest of the century, wiping out three quarters of Europe. Buboes – hideous swellings on the neck and groin – arrived with high fever and haemorrhaging: half of all victims died within a week. It has not been a serious problem since the development of antibiotics. Nor is it likely to break out in a stable society with reasonable health standards. The problem is that after an earthquake a society ceases to be stable, and the health services tend to collapse along with the walls.

Tim Radford
The Guardian, September 1994

Professor John Beringer, School of Biological Sciences, University of Bristol

My interest in biology and the world around me was stimulated while at the equivalent of primary school in the USA. At secondary school in England I was rather a poor pupil, obtaining only a few O-level passes and leaving after the first year in the sixth form, where I was studying English and History A-levels. While at school I worked on a local farm and decided to study for a Diploma in Agriculture in Edinburgh, which I obtained in 1965.

The Diploma course re-kindled my interest in biology, so I spent a year obtaining university entrance qualifications and started a degree in biochemistry at Edinburgh University. After the first year I decided to change to microbiology and graduated with an honours degree in 1970. On graduation I was keen to take a job in industry, but was persuaded that it would be wiser to obtain a PhD first. This led to ten exciting years at the John Innes Institute in Norwich, working on the bacterium *Rhizobium* (see page 30), with a particular interest in the genetic basis of how it caused nodules to form on the roots of host legume plants.

Briefly, we were able to show that the genes which determine the ability to nodulate peas or clover and fix nitrogen in the nodules were not present in the chromosomes of these bacteria, but are found on smaller circles of DNA called plasmids (see page 78). Some of these plasmids can be transferred at high frequency between different strains of *Rhizobium* in the laboratory. This suggested that in nature these genes move between strains in the soil. I am now looking to see if this is true and am examining populations isolated from the same soil in 1970 and 1994 to see whether the same strains are present. Both of these procedures depend upon recent developments in DNA technology which make the isolation, sequencing and characterisation of DNA relatively simple.

In 1980 I moved to Rothamsted Experimental Station in Harpenden, as Head of the Soil Microbiology Department. This move coincided with a dramatic change in the funding of basic science and I had to learn how to manage science with a dwindling budget and a need to cut staff. At Rothamsted I became convinced that the 'new' techniques of genetic engineering were going to revolutionise agriculture, medicine and the food industry because scientists would be able to produce organisms with combinations of characteristics from different species. I had the good fortune to become a member of a committee established to examine whether it was safe to release such organisms into the environment and to advise the government. Since 1987 I have chaired this committee (now called the Advisory Committee on Releases to the Environment or ACRE).

In 1984 I moved to the University of Bristol where I have at different times been Head of the Molecular Genetics Unit, Head of the Department of Microbiology and Head of the Department of Botany. My present job is about 30% teaching, 40% research and 30% activities relating to the regulation of genetic engineering.

Despite the cuts in funding and the job losses that have affected all scientists over the last 14 years, I consider myself to have been most fortunate to have chosen a career in science. I have had almost too many opportunities to travel around the world, have met and worked with very many different and interesting people, and have more recently had the opportunity to become involved in what promises to be the most exciting development in science ever – genetic engineering. Within the next 25 years almost all crops will carry genes from other species which will enable them to grow better and resist diseases. Many human diseases will be curable through the use of medicines from genetically modified microorganisms, or by the introduction of a functional gene in cases where defective genes are the cause of the disease. *Continued overleaf*

There is much yet to learn about the risks of using such organisms and how to handle biotechnology to ensure that what is done is ethical and in the best interests of humanity and the planet. A good example of the type of problem that must be faced is a recent application to ACRE to release an insect virus which was genetically modified to contain a scorpion toxin. The people doing this work hope that natural control agents of pest species, such as this virus, can be modified to make them more efficient and thus able to replace chemical pesticides. After a thorough examination, including confirmation that the scorpion toxin was specific to insects, and that the virus was not going to eliminate harmless insect species, the release was approved. There is a tremendous need for biologists who are well trained in ecology, biochemistry and molecular genetics to become involved in all aspects of the development and use of genetically modified organisms. From my own experience we biologists are extremely fortunate to be able to participate in such an exciting and worthwhile area of research and development.

■ LOOKING FORWARD

Despite the moral, ethical and safety issues associated with microbiology and biotechnology there can be no doubt that a great deal of good has come from studies in health, food and environmental research. The achievements, particularly in genetic engineering, in such a short time are remarkable. We are still in the early stages; comparatively few products have actually gone into commercial production, but many more are at the experimental, pilot or clinical trial stages. We are likely to see more people employed in biotechnology in the future as it is likely to attract huge financial investment aimed at the production of single cell proteins, drugs, human proteins and vaccines of veterinary and medical importance, and microbes able to engineer proteins, clear up pollution and even treat cancers.

Sir Walter Bodmer has written that 'the human genome project must be rated as one of the most thrilling of all scientific escapades. It is hard to see how one could get closer to our own interests, for the question of our biological lineage touches on understanding of our role in evolution, and survival as a species.'

'What genetics will finally bring is the end of the process of demystification of human beings that began with Darwin. The humility which should follow will do us no harm. At journey's end we will be able to prevent or postpone much disease, and we may better understand what we are, but we will still bear the heavy responsbility for the moral use of our genetic gifts'.
Dr William Cookson in *The Gene Hunters* (Aurum Press, 1994)

INDEX

131